SPIDER-MAN'S
GREATEST VILLAINS

D1616572

SARRA MOSSOFF — EDITOR

BOB BUDIANSKY — EDITOR IN CHIEF

BRADLEY PETER PARKER — COVER ART

ELAN M. COLF:
BLUE COLLAR WORK ETHIC, INC. — TRADE PAPERBACK DESIGN

STEVE ALEXANDROV — MANUFACTURING COORDINATOR

ALEXA CAMPOS — INTERN

SPIDER-MAN'S® GREATEST VILLAINS

Originally published in magazine form as Amazing Spider-Man Nº's 12, 13, 69, 82, 224, 316, Amazing Spider-Man Annual Nº28, Web of Spider-Man Nº38.

"THE MENACE OF..." MYSTERIO!

SPIDER-MAN

CAN WE BELIEVE OUR EYES? HAS THE AMAZING SPIDER-MAN TURNED TO CRIME?

THE EDITORS SINCERELY FEEL THAT THIS MAY WELL BE ONE OF THE MOST GRIPPING TALES OF THE YEAR!

BEFORE VERY LONG, YOU ARE ABOUT TO MEET A STARTLINGLY DIFFERENT BREED OF ARCH-VILLAIN! EXPECT THE UNEXPECTED WHEN YOU SEE... "MYSTERIO!"

STAN LEE—WRITER
STEVE DITKO—ARTIST
ART SIMEK—LETTERER

OUR TALE BEGINS WITH THE SHOCKING SUDDEN-NESS OF A SUMMER STORM, AS WE SEE...

HELP! POLICE! I'VE BEEN ROBBED!

THERE HE GOES! HE'S GETTING AWAY!

DID YOU RECOGNIZE HIM??

OF COURSE! IT WAS SPIDER-MAN!

NOBODY ELSE CAN LEAP OR CLIMB SHEER WALLS LIKE THAT!

WATCHMEN! ON THE ROOF! WELL, THIS WILL TAKE CARE OF THEM!

LOOK OUT-- HE'S TANGLING US UP IN THAT WEB OF HIS!

HURRY-- WE'VE GOT TO CUT OURSELVES FREE!

TOO LATE! HE'S GETTING AWAY!

SECONDS LATER, HIDDEN BY A SLOW, ROLLING FOG WHICH SPREADS OVER THE CITY, BLOTTING OUT THE MOONLIGHT, THE COLORFUL FIGURE DRIFTS SILENTLY TO THE GROUND, USING A HASTILY IMPROVISED PARACHUTE MADE OF THIN, STRONG WEBBING!

THEN, AFTER THE WATCHMEN HAVE FREED THEMSELVES...

HE GOT AWAY, BUT AT LEAST WE KNOW WHO IT WAS! IT WAS SPIDER-MAN!

WE'LL GET HIM SOONER OR LATER! BUT I NEVER THOUGHT HE'D REALLY TURN TO CRIME!

THE NEXT DAY, SCENES LIKE THIS TAKE PLACE ALL OVER THE NATION...

READ ALL ABOUT IT! SPIDER-MAN WANTED BY POLICE!

IT'S UNBELIEVABLE! WHY WOULD HE DO IT?

HE PROBABLY DECIDED TO CASH IN ON ALL HIS SUPER-POWERS-- THE CRUMMY CROOK!

MY CHILDREN HAD ALWAYS ADMIRED HIM! THIS WILL BE SUCH A SHOCK TO THEM!

IT'S A GREAT SHOCK TO ALL OF US!

HE MUST BE NUTS IF HE THINKS HE CAN GET AWAY WITH A ONE-MAN CRIME WAVE, NO MATTER HOW POWERFUL HE IS!

THE POLICE WILL SURE HAVE A TOUGH JOB GETTING HIM! BUT THEY'LL DO IT, SOONER OR LATER!

AND, IN THE OFFICE OF J. JONAH JAMESON, PUBLISHER OF NOW MAGAZINE AND THE DAILY BUGLE...

FIND ALL THE OLD EDITORIALS I WROTE, ACCUSING SPIDER-MAN OF BEING A MENACE! I WANT TO REPRINT THEM NOW, SO PEOPLE CAN SEE HOW RIGHT I WAS!

I CAN'T BELIEVE THIS OF SPIDER-MAN! I STILL REMEMBER HOW HE ONCE SAVED MY LIFE....!

AND, IN THE SCHOOL YARD OF MIDTOWN HIGH...

SPIDER-MAN SURE HAD ALL OF US FOOLED!

WHEN I THINK HOW WE MADE A HERO OF HIM--WHAT FOOLS WE WERE!

GEE, I DON'T KNOW, LIZ! WE CAN'T BE POSITIVE! HE MAY STILL BE INNOCENT!

KNOCK IT OFF, FLASH! HE'S GUILTY AND YOU KNOW IT!

AND NOW, THE MOMENT WE'VE BEEN WAITING FOR! LET'S VISIT SPIDER-MAN HIMSELF-- IN HIS EVERYDAY IDENTITY AS PETER PARKER, TEEN-AGE STUDENT...

THIS IS IMPOSSIBLE! IT'S INSANE! I KNOW I DIDN'T COMMIT THAT CRIME! AND YET-- THOSE WITNESSES! THAT EVIDENCE!

IT COULDN'T HAVE BEEN AN IMPOSTOR! NOBODY ELSE CAN SHOOT A WEB AS I DO-- OR CLIMB SHEER WALLS THE WAY I CAN WITH MY SPIDER POWER!!

THERE'S ONLY ONE OTHER ANSWER-- BUT IT'S TOO AWFUL TO THINK ABOUT--

AM I BECOMING A SPLIT-PERSONALITY?? LIKE DR. JEKYLL AND MR. HYDE?? PERHAPS-- PERHAPS I DID IT IN MY SLEEP-- WITHOUT KNOWING?!!

3

MINUTES LATER, IN THE KITCHEN...

GOSH! SORRY, AUNT MAY--THAT'S THE SECOND DISH I'VE DROPPED TODAY!

PETER DEAR, YOU DON'T SEEM TO BE YOURSELF! IS ANYTHING WRONG?

YOU'RE NOT WORRIED BECAUSE OUR SAVINGS ACCOUNT IS ALMOST GONE, AND IT'S GETTING HARDER TO PAY THE MORTGAGE EACH MONTH, ARE YOU? WE'LL MAKE OUT SOMEHOW, DEAR!

I KNOW, AUNT MAY! MAYBE I'VE BEEN STUDYING TOO HARD! I'LL JUST TRY TO GET SOME SLEEP!

AND, AS PETER GOES UP TO HIS ROOM...

THE POOR DEAR! I WORRY ABOUT HIM SO! HE'S NOT AS ROUGH AND THICK-SKINNED AS MOST OTHER BOYS! HE'S SENSITIVE--AND HE WORRIES MORE THAN HE'LL ADMIT!

AUNT MAY IS CORRECT! PETER PARKER IS WORRIED--ABOUT SOMETHING SHE'D NEVER SUSPECT!

I NEVER THOUGHT THIS WOULD HAPPEN TO ME! I-I'M AFRAID TO SHUT MY EYES--TO GO TO SLEEP!

BUT, EVENTUALLY, SLEEP DOES COME TO PETER PARKER, AND --THE NEXT MORNING, WHEN HE AWAKES...

BULLETIN! SPIDER-MAN HAS STRUCK AGAIN DURING THE NIGHT!

OH NO!!

WHAT'S HAPPENING TO ME??! AM I LOSING MY MIND?? MAYBE I'M GOING MAD--DOING THINGS I CAN'T REMEMBER THE NEXT MORNING?!!

THERE'S ONLY ONE THING TO DO--ONLY ONE WAY TO FIND OUT--

AND SO, A SHORT TIME LATER, IN THE OFFICE OF A NEARBY PSYCHIATRIST...

DON'T BE ALARMED, DOC! I JUST WANT TO KNOW ONE THING! CAN A PERSON DO SOMETHING IN HIS SLEEP THAT HE'D NEVER DO AWAKE?

SPIDER-MAN! IF I CAN MAKE A PATIENT OUT OF HIM, I'LL MAKE MEDICAL HISTORY! IMAGINE, A MYSTERIOUS SUPER HERO WHO'S A MENTAL CASE!

I THINK I CAN HELP YOU! JUST COME DOWN FROM THAT WALL AND LIE DOWN ON THE COUCH! I'LL TRY TO PROBE INTO YOUR SUB-CONSCIOUS! DON'T BE NERVOUS!

OKAY, DOC-- BUT NO TRICKS, HEAR?

JUST MAKE YOURSELF COMFORTABLE HERE! RELAX--AND THEN TELL ME ANYTHING THAT COMES INTO YOUR HEAD!

I APPRECIATE THIS, DOCTOR! IF YOU CAN HELP ME, I--

OH *NO!* WHAT A *MISTAKE* I ALMOST MADE! IF I JUST RELAX AND SAY WHATEVER I THINK OF, I'M LIABLE TO GIVE AWAY MY SECRET IDENTITY! I DON'T *DARE!*

SORRY, DOC--I JUST CHANGED MY MIND! IT LOOKS LIKE I'LL HAVE TO FIND *ANOTHER* SOLUTION! SORRY TO HAVE BOTHERED YOU!

WAIT! COME *BACK!* YOU'RE THE KIND OF PATIENT EVERY PSYCHIATRIST *DREAMS* OF! *STOP!*

A SHORT TIME LATER, AT THE OFFICES OF THE *DAILY BUGLE*...

PETER, WHAT'S *WRONG!* YOU LOOK SO DEJECTED...!

NOTHING, BETTY! I'M OKAY!

YOU'RE PROBABLY WORRIED BECAUSE YOU HAVEN'T SOLD ANY NEWS PHOTOS TO MR. JAMESON LATELY! OH, PETER, IF ONLY YOU'D FIND SOME DIFFERENT TYPE OF WORK!

LAY OFF, WILLYA, BETTY? I'M IN NO MOOD TO BE *PREACHED* TO!

YOU'RE ALWAYS SAYING THAT IT'S TOO *DANGEROUS* TO TRY TO TAKE EX-CLUSIVE CRIME PHOTOS! I DON'T TELL YOU HOW TO LIVE *YOUR* LIFE--DON'T BUTT INTO *MINE!*

Y-YOU NEVER *SPOKE* TO ME THAT WAY BEFORE !!

THEN, PETER ENTERS THE PRIVATE OFFICE OF A JUBILANT J. JONAH JAMESON...

LOOK AT THESE LETTERS --THESE TELEGRAMS! THE PUBLIC FINALLY SAYS I WAS *RIGHT* ABOUT SPIDER-MAN! WHAT A GREAT *TRIUMPH* THIS IS FOR ME!

I'M GLAD YOU'RE IN A GOOD MOOD, MISTER JAMESON! I, EH, NEED A *LOAN!* MY AUNT HAS A MORTGAGE PAYMENT TO MAKE, AND WE'RE A LITTLE SHORT...

WHY TELL *ME?* I'M NOT A BANK! YOU KNOW MY RULE, PARKER--I DON'T LEND MONEY! I'M *BUSY* NOW! YOU KNOW WHERE THE DOOR IS!

BUT I'M NOT ASKING FOR *MUCH*-- JUST A LITTLE TILL I GET SOME PICTURES FOR YOU!

DON'T TRY TO TAKE ADVANTAGE OF ME BECAUSE I'M SO SOFT-HEARTED! THE ANSWER IS *NO!* UNLESS-- YOU WANT TO SELL ME THE SECRET OF *HOW* YOU TAKE THOSE GREAT CRIME PHOTOS OF YOURS?

NO DICE!

I *KNOW* YOU MUST HAVE SOME SORT OF SPECIAL CAMERA--!!

IMAGINE IF I EVER TOLD HIM I WEAR IT IN MY BELT-- WHEN I'M DRESSED AS *SPIDER-MAN,* SWINGING OVER THE CITY ON MY WEB!

THANKS FOR *NOTHING,* MR. JAMESON!

FINALLY...

I KNOW I SHOULDN'T DO THIS WHILE THE WHOLE CITY IS HUNTING FOR *SPIDER-MAN!*

BUT THE ONLY WAY I CAN GET THE MORTGAGE MONEY FOR AUNT MAY IS TO TAKE SOME NEWS PIX WHICH JJJ WILL PAY ME FOR!

IF I'M *LUCKY,* I MAY SPOT A CRIME BEING COMMITTED WHILE I SWING THRU TOWN...

LOOK! IT'S *SPIDER-MAN!*

AFTER *HIM!*

CALL THE *POLICE!*

DON'T LET HIM GET AWAY!

IT'S WORSE THAN I *THOUGHT!* THE PUBLIC *HATES* ME NOW!

AND THE TERRIBLE THING ABOUT IT IS-- I DON'T KNOW IF THEY'RE *RIGHT!*

I CAN'T MAKE THE MONEY I NEED-- AND I MAY BE COMMITTING CRIMES WITHOUT *KNOWING* IT! *BOY!* LIFE SURE IS A BOWL OF CHERRIES!

6

THE NEXT DAY, ON THE WAY TO HIGH SCHOOL...

I DON'T KNOW WHAT TO WORRY ABOUT FIRST! PAYING THE MORTGAGE, OR WONDERING IF I'M A SLEEP-WALKING CRIMINAL?!!

PETER! WAIT FOR ME!

I'VE BEEN WANTING TO SHOW YOU MY NEW HAIRDO! DO YOU LIKE IT?

SURE, LIZ! IT'S REAL NICE!

OF ALL TIMES TO HAVE TO TALK ABOUT A GAL'S HAIR!

WHAT NUTTY TIMING! FOR MONTHS LIZ WOULDN'T GIVE ME A TUMBLE, BUT SINCE I'VE BEEN DATING BETTY, LIZ HAS GOTTEN A CRUSH ON ME!

YOU LOOK UPSET, PETER! IS ANYTHING WRONG?

WOW! IS THAT QUESTION THE UNDERSTATEMENT OF THE YEAR!!

NAW, EVERYTHING'S GREAT, LIZ! IF IT GETS ANY BETTER I'LL SHOOT MYSELF!

OH, PETER! I ALWAYS KNEW YOU HAD A GREAT SENSE OF HUMOR!

MEANWHILE, A FEW YARDS AWAY...

QUIT KIDDIN', FLASH! YOU DON'T REALLY THINK SPIDER-MAN IS INNOCENT, DO YOU?

YOU'RE DARN RIGHT I DO! LET ME TELL YOU--

HEY! LOOK AT THAT!! WOW-WEEE!

GOSH, LIZ, I ALMOST DIDN'T RECOGNIZE YOU! YOU'RE BEAUTIFUL NOW!

REALLY, MISTER THOMPSON?? AND WHAT WAS I BEFORE, PRAY TELL??

POOR FLASH! HE ALWAYS SAYS THE WRONG THING!!

MEANWHILE, AT J. JONAH JAMESON'S OFFICE...

WHAT DID YOU CALL THIS MEETING FOR, J.J.?

SOME NUT SENT ME A NOTE SAYING HE COULD GET RID OF SPIDER-MAN SINGLE-HANDED! I TOLD HIM TO COME UP HERE AND PROVE IT!

LOOK AT THE DOOR....!

I AM MYSTERIO!

WHAT A GETUP! HE'S CORNIER-LOOKING THAN SPIDER-MAN!

9

THERE IS A *REASON* FOR MY *DISGUISE!* IF THE UNDERWORLD EVER FINDS OUT ABOUT MY *"POWERS,"* THEY MIGHT TRY TO STOP ME BY THREATENING MY FAMILY!

POWERS? WHAT POWERS?

HOW DO WE KNOW IT'S NOT A *TRICK?* YOU COULD BE SPIDER-MAN *HIMSELF* UNDER THAT FISHBOWL!

YOU WILL LEARN SOON ENOUGH THAT I *MEAN* WHAT I SAY! *MYSTERIO* DOES NOT LIE!

I MUST GO NOW! IF YOU WISH TO END THE MENACE OF SPIDER-MAN, FOLLOW THE INSTRUCTIONS IN THIS ENVELOPE!

REMEMBER, ALTHOUGH SPIDER-MAN HAS GREAT POWERS, THE POWER OF *MYSTERIO* IS EVEN GREATER!

WHERE'D THAT *SMOKE* COME FROM?? H-HE'S *DIS-APPEARING!*

HE'S *GONE!* WH-WHAT KIND OF A PERSON *WAS* HE??

QUIET! I'LL SEE WHAT THIS LETTER SAYS...

I DON'T *GET* IT! BUT IT MUST MAKE SENSE, OR MYSTERIO WOULDN'T HAVE GONE TO ALL THIS TROUBLE!

PRINT A NOTICE IN THE DAILY BUGLE SAYING: IF SPIDER-MAN WANTS TO LEARN THE TRUTH ABOUT HIMSELF, HE SHOULD MEET MYSTERIO ATOP THE BROOKLYN BRIDGE!

DID YOU SEE *THAT??* THE LETTER VANISHED-- IN A PUFF OF SMOKE!

Y'KNOW, JJ, IF SPIDER-MAN *CAN* BE BEATEN, I'VE GOT A HUNCH THAT MYSTERIO IS THE ONE TO *DO* IT!

WELL, WE'VE GOT NOTHING TO LOSE! I'LL *PRINT* THAT NOTICE! AND IF IT MEANS THE END OF SPIDER-MAN, I'LL BECOME A *HERO* TO THE PEOPLE OF THIS CITY!

THAT'S RIGHT, J J!

8

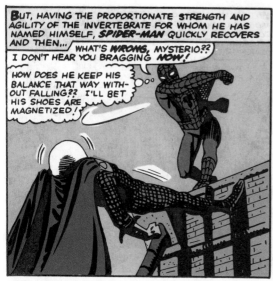

THE LONGER I STAY THERE, THE MORE PUNISHMENT I'LL TAKE!

ONLY ONE THING TO DO-- AND *THIS* IS IT!

THEN, AS SPIDER-MAN HITS THE WATER BELOW, THE DRAMATIC FIGURE OF *MYSTERIO* APPEARS ONCE AGAIN THRU THE BILLOWING MIST...

I'VE *WON!* IF *SPIDER-MAN* COULDN'T DEFEAT ME, THEN *NOBODY* CAN! NOW *MYSTERIO* IS SUPREME!

*S*ECONDS LATER, POLICE HELICOPTERS APPEAR ON THE SCENE...

SPIDER-MAN HAS BEEN DEFEATED BY MYSTERIO! WE ARE PROCEEDING WITH "OPERATION PICK-UP"...

-*WHEW!*- WHAT A DROP! UH OH! POLICE WHIRLY-BIRDS! IF I DON'T MOVE FAST I'LL BE CAUGHT!

SPIDER-MAN SWIFTLY FASHIONS AN AIR-TIGHT WEB HELMET, AND PLACES IT OVER HIS HEAD...

THIS'LL ENABLE ME TO HOLD MY BREATH UNDER-WATER LONG ENOUGH TO GET TO SAFETY!

*M*INUTES LATER, AT A LONELY PIER...

WELL, *ONE* THING IS CERTAIN-- A DEFEAT LIKE *THIS* WILL SURE KEEP ME FROM EVER GETTING TOO *CONCEITED!*

*T*HEN, AFTER SILENTLY REACH-ING HIS HOME...

BUT THE DAY WASN'T A *TOTAL* LOSS! I *DID* LEARN THE ANSWER TO *ONE* OF THE THINGS THAT'S BEEN WORRYING ME!

12

THE NEXT DAY, CROWDS LINE FIFTH AVENUE AS A MOTORCADE DRIVES BY, LED BY A HAPPILY WAVING COSTUMED FIGURE...

MYSTERIO *DESERVES* THIS PARADE! AT LAST WE HAVE SOMEONE WHO CAN BEAT *SPIDER-MAN!*

HOORAY FOR MYSTERIO! SPIDER-MAN WON'T *DARE* PULL ANY MORE CRIMES IN THIS CITY *NOW!*

AND AMONG THE TEEN-AGERS WATCHING THE PARADE, WE FIND...

STILL THINK SPIDER-MAN'S SO GREAT, FLASH?

DARN *RIGHT* I DO! MYSTERIO'S JUST A BIG PUBLICITY HOUND, IF YOU ASK ME! MY DOUGH IS *STILL* ON SPIDER-MAN!

Y'KNOW SOMETHING, FLASH? YOU'RE NOT AS DUMB AS YOU *LOOK!* IN FACT, YOU'RE *OKAY*, FELLA!

LOOK, PUNY PARKER, I DON'T NEED COMPLIMENTS FROM *YOU!* AND WHILE WE'RE TALKIN', I WANNA WARN YOU TO STAY AWAY FROM LIZ ALLAN! SHE'S *MY* GIRL FRIEND!

REALLY? TOO BAD *SHE* DOESN'T SEEM TO THINK SO! BUT DON'T WORRY, BRIGHT EYES, YOU CAN *HAVE* HER!

A SHORT TIME LATER, AT THE OFFICE OF J. JONAH JAMESON...

I WANT THE MEMBERS OF MY STAFF TO MEET MYSTERIO, THE MAN WHO BEAT SPIDER-MAN!

MYSTERIO IS A *REAL* CRIME-FIGHTER! HE'S NOT AFRAID TO MEET PEOPLE AND TO BE INTERVIEWED, AS THAT COWARDLY SPIDER-MAN WAS!

AND ONCE MYSTERIO HAS DEFEATED SPIDER-MAN FOR GOOD, HE WILL REVEAL HIS TRUE IDENTITY EXCLUSIVELY TO *MY* NEWSPAPER! IT'LL BE THE SCOOP OF THE CENTURY FOR ME! *RIGHT*, MYSTERIO?

RIGHT! JUST SO LONG AS YOU REMEMBER THE *MONEY* YOU PROMISED ME!

MYSTERIO, I WANT YOU TO MEET PETER PARKER! DON'T LET HIS *AGE* FOOL YOU! DESPITE HIS YOUTH, HE'S THE BEST PHOTOGRAPHER I'VE GOT! I'LL EXPECT HIM TO TAKE SOME GREAT PICTURES OF YOUR NEXT FIGHT WITH SPIDER-MAN!

I'LL TRY NOT TO DISAPPOINT YOU-- *BOTH* OF YOU!

13

BUT, UNNOTICED BY ANYONE IN THE ROOM, PARKER'S LEFT HAND CONTAINS A SMALL ELECTRONICALLY TREATED SPIDER-PIN*...

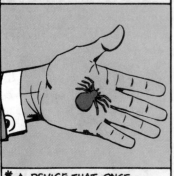

* A DEVICE THAT, ONCE ATTACHED, ENABLES HIM TO TRACK SOMEONE OR SOMETHING.

WHILE NO ONE IS PAYING ATTENTION, I'LL JUST SLIP MY LITTLE SPIDER-DEVICE IN THE FOLDS OF MYSTERIO'S CLOAK...LIKE THIS!

NOW I'LL BE ABLE TO TRACE HIS MOVEMENTS! THERE'S MORE TO MYSTERIO THAN MEETS THE EYES-- AND I'M GONNA FIND OUT WHAT IT IS!

THEN, AS PETER LEAVES JAMESON'S OFFICE...

I'M GLAD TO SEE YOU SMILING AGAIN, PETER! ARE YOU CELEBRATING SPIDER-MAN'S DEFEAT, ALSO?

NOT EXACTLY, BETTY!

IN FACT, I'M NOT SO SURE THAT SPIDER-MAN HAS BEEN DEFEATED! WELL, I HAVE TO RUSH NOW! SEE YOU LATER...

YOU'RE NOT SURE--?? BUT...

HMM! HE'S NEVER BEEN SO ANXIOUS TO LEAVE ME BEFORE! CAN HE HAVE MET ANOTHER GIRL? I'VE NOTICED A PRETTY BLONDE WITH HIM OCCASIONALLY...

OH, STOP IT, BETTY BRANT! YOU'RE BECOMING JEALOUS!

WHILE BEHIND THE DOOR TO JAMESON'S OFFICE...

I SHALL LEAVE YOU NOW, JAMESON. IN MY OWN MANNER! FAREWELL-- TILL NEXT TIME!

HE'S GONE! FOR HEAVEN'S SAKE, JJJ, HOW DOES HE DO IT?

WHO CARES? THE IMPORTANT THING IS THAT I'VE FINALLY FOUND SOMEONE WHO CAN BEAT SPIDER-MAN! I FEEL LIKE CELEBRATING!

BUT JAMESON MIGHT NOT FEEL SO TRIUMPHANT IF HE COULD SEE A DRAMATIC FIGURE ON A NEARBY ROOFTOP, WAITING TO RECEIVE THE ELECTRONIC SIGNAL FROM HIS HIDDEN SPIDER-PIN!

AH, MY SPYING DEVICE IS BEGINNING TO REGISTER NOW!

14

16

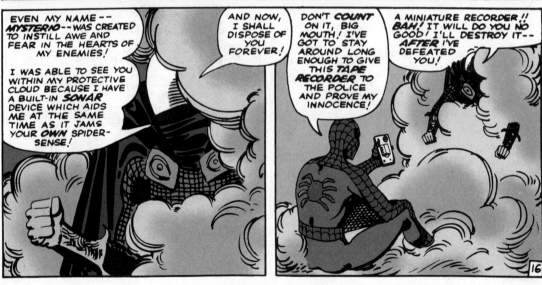

BUT, IN A SPLIT-SECOND, SPIDER-MAN FLIPS BACKWARDS, OUT OF THE SPREADING MIST!

NOT *THIS* TIME, MYSTERIO! REMEMBER ONE THING -- *YOUR* POWER IS ARTIFICIAL -- BUT *MINE* IS NATURAL!!

AND I'LL BET ON *MY* NATURAL SPIDER-POWERS *ANY* TIME!

I'VE GOT TO CIRCLE AROUND -- TRY TO FIND HIM WITHIN THE MIST!

HAVE TO KEEP MOVING *FAST!* CAN'T LOSE THE ADVANTAGE!

HE'S NOT HERE -- OR HERE! BUT HE'S GOT TO BE NEARBY!

IF I KEEP SWINGING, THEN SOONER OR LATER I'LL -- *AHHH*, I WAS RIGHT! *THERE* HE IS!

WHAM!

THEN, AS MYSTERIO GOES SLIDING ALONG THE FLOOR INTO THE NEXT-DOOR STUDIO...

OKAY, QUIET ON THE SET! LET'S ROLL 'EM! *HUH? WAIT --* WHAT'S *THAT??*

GET THAT GUY *OUT* OF HERE! HE'S IN THE WRONG MOVIE!

17

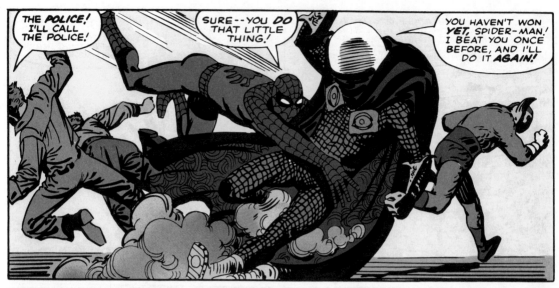

WITH MY SPIDER-SENSE COMPLETELY OPERATIONAL NOW, IT'S A BREEZE TO MAKE MY WAY THRU THE MIST AND LEAVE THE TV STUDIO UNSEEN BY ANYONE!

AND, WHEN THE STRANGE MIST FINALLY CLEARS...

FOR THE LUVVA PETE!! WHERE'D THEY GO??!

YOU NINCOMPOOP!! THE GREATEST ACTION SCENE IN HISTORY, AND YOU DIDN'T EVEN GET IT ON FILM!!!

B-BUT THEY WEREN'T MEMBERS OF THE CAST!! PROBABLY DIDN'T EVEN BELONG TO THE UNION!

AND, A FEW MINUTES LATER, AT POLICE HEADQUARTERS...

I HEARD MYSTERIO WAS HERE! WH-WHAT HAPPENED, CHIEF??

IT'S INCREDIBLE, MR. JAMESON! SPIDER-MAN BROUGHT HIM IN, AND WE HAVE A FULL CONFESSION ON TAPE FROM MYSTERIO'S OWN LIPS! HE'S THE CRIMINAL WE'VE BEEN SEEKING! SPIDER-MAN IS INNOCENT!!

OUR MEN ARE PICKING UP ALL THE STOLEN LOOT NOW, CHIEF-- THANKS TO SPIDER-MAN!

MYSTERIO IS THE GUILTY ONE?? SPIDER-MAN IS INNOCENT???!

AND AFTER ALL I WROTE IN MY NEWSPAPERS!! I-I'LL BE A LAUGHING STOCK--AGAIN!! OH NO!!

THEN, WHEN JAMESON RETURNS TO HIS OFFICE...

CANCEL ALL MY APPOINTMENTS, MISS BRANT! AND SEND DOWN FOR A BOTTLE OF ASPIRIN-- A BIG BOTTLE!

YES SIR! PETER PARKER WAS JUST IN! HE LEFT SOME PHOTOS FOR YOU!

HMMPH! A LOT OF GOOD PHOTOS CAN DO ME NOW! I'LL--HUH?? WHAT ARE THOSE?!!

FIGHT SCENES!! SPIDER-MAN AND MYSTERIO!!

THAT LUCKY PARKER!! HE MUST HAVE BEEN THERE JUST AT THE RIGHT TIME! THESE PICTURES ARE PERFECT FOR THE FRONT PAGE! I'M SAVED!

STOP THE PRESSES! WE'RE PUTTING OUT AN EXTRA!

21

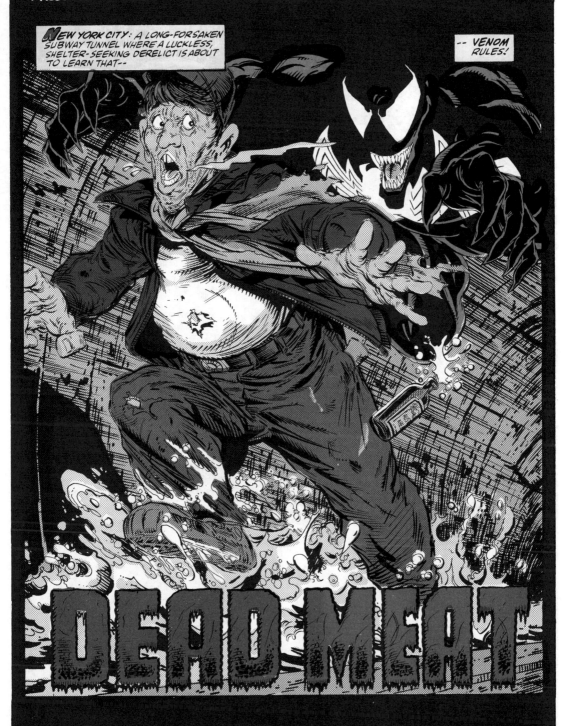

26

27

A DESTINY BEGUN WHEN *SPIDER-MAN* DESTROYED MY LIFE! I SOUGHT SOLACE IN SUICIDE, BUT YOU STOPPED ME, MY EBON FRIEND. YOU SAVED ME. *JOINED* ME.

AND OUR SHARED HATRED FOR THAT WALL-CRAWLING MONSTER MADE US ONE.

THE ENTITY THE WORLD HAS COME TO KNOW AS *VENOM!*

SAFE TO PURSUE OUR *DESTINY!*

NOW, WE MUST PREPARE. THESE WEIGHTS ARE RUSTED, DUST-COVERED. BUT THEY WILL *SUFFICE.*

FOR WHILE *YOUR* POWER IS INHERENT, *MY* MUSCLES MUST BE *EARNED!* AND WE MUST BOTH BE AT OUR FULLEST POSSIBLE STRENGTH--

--SO THAT WE MAY RIP SPIDER-MAN INTO THE SMALLEST POSSIBLE *PIECES!*

SPEAK OF THE DEVIL, AND YOU'LL HEAR THE RUSTLE OF HIS WINGS.

OR IN THIS CASE, THE CLICK OF HIS *SHUTTER!*

MY CAMERA HAS AN "AUTOMATIC" SETTING. *IT* SHOULD BE TAKING PICTURES WHILE *I* HELP THE GOOD GUYS!

BUT I'VE SEARCHED ALL MORNING FOR ACTION I COULD PHOTOGRAPH BUT NOT GET *INVOLVED* IN. AND NOW THAT I'VE *FOUND* IT--

--I'D BETTER TAKE ADVANTAGE OF IT! BESIDES, THE POLICE SHOULDN'T HAVE ANY TROUBLE NABBING THAT BANK ROBBER. I MEAN, IT'S NOT LIKE HE HAD A *GUN* OR--

"..NUTS.

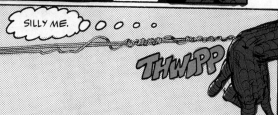

IT'S HARD ON MY EGO, BUT REMAINING ANONYMOUS IS THE ONLY WAY I CAN MAKE A *LIVING* THESE DAYS!

WHAT WITH *J. JONAH JAMESON* ACTING EVEN WEIRDER THAN USUAL--

--NOT BUYING SPIDER-MAN PHOTOS FOR *THE DAILY BUGLE* FROM ANYONE BUT *NICK KATZENBERG!*

A FELLOW WITH A DECIDEDLY *ANTI-SPIDEY* BIAS!

AND MY INCOME'S BECOME EVEN MORE IMPORTANT SINCE *MARY JANE* AND I GOT EVICTED FROM OUR CONDO, WITH HER MONEY TIED UP IN *LEGAL* HASSLES--

--PAYING FOR MY GRADUATE STUDIES, AND PUTTING ASIDE FOR A NEW APARTMENT, IS STRAINING *MY* SAVINGS TO THE BREAKING POINT!

I'VE BEEN FORCED TO FIND NEWS THAT DOESN'T HAVE *ME* IN IT!

MAYBE I SHOULD LOOK FOR *OTHER* COSTUMED TYPES TO PHOTOGRAPH. AT LEAST JONAH HASN'T BLACK-BALLED ANYONE *ELSE*.

YET!

AH, WELL, BETTER CHANGE INTO THE *CIVILIAN CLOTHES* IN MY *WEBBING BUNDLE* --

-- AND LET *PETER PARKER* PEDDLE HIS *WARES!*

INSIDE, AT GLORIA GRANT'S WORK STATION...

HI, PETER! HERE ARE THOSE *CHANGE OF ADDRESS* NOTICES YOU ASKED ME TO RUN OFF.

GREAT!

SO HOW'S IT WORKING OUT, LIVING WITH YOUR *AUNT MAY* AGAIN -- *UHP!* LATER, PETE. MY *LUNCH DATE'S* HERE!

O.K., GLORY, THANKS FOR THE COPIES.

YOU DIDN'T MAKE THOSE ON THE *OFFICE* COPIER, DID YOU?

'LO, NICK.

USING *COMPANY PROPERTY* FOR PERSONAL NEEDS? DOES *JONAH* KNOW ABOUT THIS?

DOES *GERALDO* KNOW WHAT YOU USE TO SATISFY *YOUR* PERSONAL NEEDS, KATZENBERG?

HMPH!

MJ'S A REAL TROUPER. SHE'S WORRIED ABOUT THE *DOWNSWING* HER MODELING CAREER HAS TAKEN, AND FEELS BAD THAT WE WERE EVICTED BECAUSE SOME JEALOUS LUNATIC HAD A *CRUSH* ON HER. BUT SHE'S REALLY HIDING IT--

--EH? *SPIDER-SENSE!* USUALLY WARNS OF *DANGER!*

BUT LATELY IT'S BEEN BUZZING WHEN GLORY'S NEW BOYFRIEND IS AROUND!

SURE WISH I KNEW *WHY.*

BUT WHILE PETER PARKER PONDERS, A LITHE FORM LEAPS FROM AN UPPER WEST-SIDE ROOF-TOP--

--LANDING ON A BALCONY AT THE *BEDFORD TOWERS,* A TERRACE ONCE USED BY SPIDER-MAN FOR CLANDESTINE ENTRY, AND NOW USED BY--

-- THE BLACK CAT!

NO FURNITURE? HE'S MOVED OUT?!

BLAST!

WHEN I GOT BACK FROM EUROPE, SPIDER HAD MOVED FROM OUR OLD APARTMENT ON CHELSEA STREET, AND IT TOOK ME *WEEKS* TO TRACK HIM DOWN HERE!

NOW HE'S GONE *AGAIN!*

34

WE WERE IN LOVE, BUT I FLEW THE COOP, EVEN THOUGH I'D LOST MY *BAD LUCK* POWERS, AND KNEW THEY WOULDN'T BE A DANGER TO SPIDER!

I GOT MIXED UP WITH THAT SNAKE CALLED *THE FOREIGNER* FOR A WHILE, BUT NOW I KNOW THAT SPIDER AND I WERE *MEANT* TO BE TOGETHER IF ONLY I CAN FIND--

SPIDER...?

NO! COSTUME'S RIGHT, BUT HE'S TOO BIG! TOO...

...EVIL!

WHERE IS HE?

PARKER'S FLED HIS LAIR! BUT YOU KNOW *WHO* HE IS--YOU MUST KNOW *WHERE* HE IS!

TELL ME!

THRAK

THE ONLY THING I'M TELLIN' YOU, BUSTER, IS WHERE TO *GO!*

AND I *DON'T* THINK YOU'LL LIKE IT!

35

UH-OH! HE'S GOT *WEBBING*, JUST LIKE SPIDER! TOO STRONG FOR ME TO BREAK!

BUT FORTUNATELY, THE STEEL CHAIN HOLDING THAT CHANDELIER UP--

--ISN'T!

CRIKLEEESH!

YYYYYAAAGGGGWOMAN!

KRUNCH

36

37

38

BUT CALLS TO GOVERNMENT AGENCIES ARE REFERRED TO *OTHER* AGENCIES, THEN OTHERS STILL. UNTIL FINALLY...

LOOK, I'M TIRED OF GETTING THE RUN-AROUND! I'M TELLING YOU THIS IS *SPIDER-MAN*, AND I WANT SOME ANSWERS!

LIKE WHY THE *MEDIA* HAVEN'T BEEN ALERTED THAT A NUT CASE CALLED *VENOM* ESCAPED FROM YOUR *HIGHLY-TOUTED VAULT!*

-- WHAT? YOU WERE TRYING TO PREVENT PANIC?

YOU SUGGEST I FILL OUT A *FORMAL COMPLAINT?!*

WAIT --! DON'T YOU *DARE* PUT ME ON HOLD! *DON'T* --

THAT MANIAC SWORE TO *KILL* ME, AND IT'D BE NICE TO HAVE A LITTLE *WARNING* WHEN --

PLAKT

HE FOUND US ON CHELSEA STREET. HE FOUND WHERE WE LIVED AT THE BEDFORD. WHAT IF HE FINDS US... *HERE?*

DON'T WORRY, MJ, VENOM WON'T *HAVE* TO FIND ME -- BECAUSE *I'M* GOING TO FIND *HIM!*

THUS, AS THE HOURS OF NIGHT CRAWL BY, SPIDER-MAN CRISSCROSSES MANHATTAN IN AN ALL-INCLUSIVE GRID.

HE DOES NOT ENJOY HIMSELF.

MAYBE MARY JANE *SHOULD* WORRY. IF VENOM FINDS OUT WHERE WE'RE STAYING, HE COULD NOT ONLY PUT *MJ* IN DANGER, BUT COULD THREATEN AUNT MAY AND THE BOARDERS AS WELL!

WHICH IS WHY I HAVE NO CHOICE-- I HAVE TO TAKE THE FIGHT TO *HIM!*

BE A LOT EASIER IF I HAD THE SLIGHTEST IDEA WHERE HE *IS!*

42

43

SPIDER-MAN IS A HERO. BUT BENEATH THE MASK, HE IS JUST A MAN. AND LIKE ALL MEN--

YAAAAAAH!

BLO'$H'T

THRUD

OKAY! SO I *PANICKED!* NOTHING LIKE THAT EVER *HAPPENED* TO ME BEFORE! I HAD TO GET *OUT!*

NOW I HAVE TO GET HOME, TAKE A SHOWER! WASH THIS... THIS *STUFF* OFF MY COSTUME! I JUST CAN'T BEAT VENOM ONE-ON-ONE!

" I'LL NEED A PLAN, MAYBE SOME HELP! BUT AT LEAST I'LL HAVE TIME TO WORK ON IT!

" THANK HEAVEN VENOM STILL DOESN'T KNOW--

"--WHERE I *LIVE!* "

WE'VE MOVED!

Please be advised that [PE]TER and MARY JANE [?] PARKER are now residing at:

[?]0 Ingram Street [Fore]st Hills, NY 11375 (718) 555-5692

THE END... FOR NOW!

AND SO, AS I'VE RARELY BEEN ONE TO PASS UP A LITTLE FUN IN THE SUN...

AWAY WE GO!

HAH! WHO NEEDS A HEALTH SPA?

WHEN YOU HAVE THE PROPORTIONATE STRENGTH, SPEED, AND AGILITY OF A SPIDER...

...THE WHOLE WORLD CAN BE YOUR GYMNASIUM!

BUT, FIVE SECONDS AND TWO MILES LATER...

UH-OH, MY SPIDER-SENSE IS STARTING TO TINGLE! THERE'S DANGER THREATENING, AND FROM THE INTENSITY OF THE BUZZ, I'D GUESS IT'S ONLY--

"--BLOCKS AWAY!"

C'MON, WILL YA? I KILT THE ALARM SYSTEM, BUT SOMEBODY'S BOUND TO CALL THE COPS!

METRO BANK

DON'T SWEAT IT, HAROLD--

DOOING

--ARNIE SPENT FIVE YEARS ON THE STOCK CAR CIRCUIT! HE'LL HAVE US IN JERSEY BEFORE ANYONE EVEN THINKS OF A PHONE!

RIGHT, ARNIE?

YOU KNOW IT, MAN!

VRRRM

WHAT THE--?!? I'VE GOT THIS BABY FLOORED, BUT WE'RE GOIN' NOWHERE!

51

MEANWHILE, AT MANHATTAN'S BELLEVUE HOSPITAL...

I'M TELLIN' YOU, MAN-- YOU MUST'A BEEN BORN UNDER A LUCKY STAR! I MEAN--

--YOU HAD MORE BROKEN BONES THAN HEINZ HAS PICKLES! I'D HAVE THOUGHT THAT AN OLD DUDE LIKE YOU WOULD'VE BEEN IN TRACTION FOR LIFE!

MY...FAMILY... HAS ALWAYS BEEN VERY RESILIENT.

YEAH? WELL, DON'T GO THINKIN' YOU'RE *TOO* RESILIENT! 'CAUSE AS SOON AS THE DOCS GIVE YOU A CLEAN BILL'A HEALTH,--

--SOME GENTLE-MEN WILL BE BY TO CONDUCT YOU TO ONE OF THE FEDERAL GOVERNMENT'S FINER PRISONS! I DON'T KNOW HOW MANY YEARS THEY GOT YOU FOR--

--BUT, AT YOUR AGE, A YEAR COULD BE A LIFE SENTENCE!

HEY, BRO! HERE'S OL' MAN TOOMES... ALL SET FOR HIS FIRST HOUR OF PHYSICAL THERAPY!

YOU JUST WATCH OUT FOR HIM, THOUGH! HE'S A PURELY DANGER-OUS CRIMINAL! WHY, HE'S LIABLE TO BEAT YA TO DEATH WITH HIS CANE!

HAH-HA-HA!

YEAH...SURE! RIGHT THIS WAY, MR. TOOMES--

--AND WE'LL SEE TO SETTING UP A THERAPY PROGRAM FOR YOU.

PLEASE EXCUSE THE MESS. THE HOSPITAL IS INSTALLING A NEW DEVICE FOR ELECTRONIC-ALLY STIMULATING THE HEALING OF BROKEN BONES--

--AND THE TECHNICIANS HAVEN'T FINISHED CONNECTING ALL THE MAGNO-ELECTRONICS YET!

WE'RE A LITTLE SHORT-HANDED TODAY. WHY DON'T YOU TAKE A SEAT, WHILE I LOOK UP YOUR RECORDS?

6

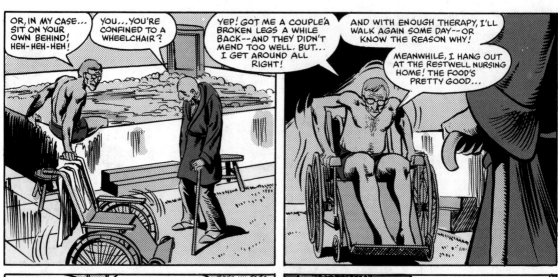

OR, IN MY CASE... SIT ON YOUR OWN BEHIND! HEH-HEH-HEH!

YOU...YOU'RE CONFINED TO A WHEELCHAIR?

YEP! GOT ME A COUPLE'A BROKEN LEGS A WHILE BACK--AND THEY DIDN'T MEND TOO WELL. BUT... I GET AROUND ALL RIGHT!

AND WITH ENOUGH THERAPY, I'LL WALK AGAIN SOME DAY--OR KNOW THE REASON WHY!

MEANWHILE, I HANG OUT AT THE RESTWELL NURSING HOME! THE FOOD'S PRETTY GOOD...

...AND I EVEN FOUND ME A SWEETIE! AND POKER PARTNERS!

YOU PLAY POKER, ADE?

WELL...

MR. LUBENSKY! YOU SHOULD HAVE WAITED FOR ME! YOU COULD HAVE FALLEN!

NOT ON YOUR LIFE! MY BALANCE IS BETTER THAN YOURS, JOHANSSON!

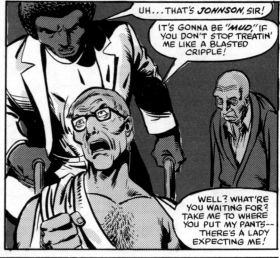

UH...THAT'S JOHNSON, SIR!

IT'S GONNA BE "MUD," IF YOU DON'T STOP TREATIN' ME LIKE A BLASTED CRIPPLE!

WELL? WHAT'RE YOU WAITING FOR? TAKE ME TO WHERE YOU PUT MY PANTS-- THERE'S A LADY EXPECTING ME!

WHATEVER YOU SAY, SIR!

AND DON'T PATRONIZE ME! I MAY BE GRAY, BUT I'M MORE ALIVE THAN YOU'LL EVER BE!

YOU'RE ONLY AS OLD AS YOU FEEL, YA KNOW!

HE'S RIGHT! HE'S SO RIGHT! I'VE LET THOSE GUARDS AND ORDERLIES CONVINCE ME THAT I'M OLD AND WASHED UP...BUT I'M NOT!

NATE HAS THE RIGHT IDEA! AGE IS ONLY A STATE OF MIND!

RIGHT NOW, I WANT A LOOK AT THE INNARDS OF THIS CONTRAPTION!

8

SORRY I WAS GONE SO LONG, FOLKS, WE'VE LOST MR. TOOMES'S RECORDS, AND I WAS TRYING TO TRACK THEM DOWN!

TOOMES?! THERE'S NO ONE BY THAT NAME HERE! THERE'S ONLY--

--THE VULTURE!

HOLEE--!

MR. TOOMES?

I THANK YOU FOR TAKING YOUR TIME, YOUNGSTER! YOU WERE GONE JUST LONG ENOUGH FOR ME TO JURY-RIG A FLYING DEVICE FROM THAT MACHINE!

NOW, GET OUT OF MY WAY!

KRAK

MUST SHIELD MYSELF WITH THESE MAKESHIFT WINGS! I DON'T WANT TO BREAK ANY MORE BONES!

KRASH

I WANT TO BE FREE! I WANT TO LIVE!

YES! THIS IS THE WAY IT WAS MEANT TO BE! ONCE I'M SAFELY AWAY, I'LL MAKE MYSELF A REAL PAIR OF WINGS--

--AND THEN, I'LL SET THIS TOWN ON ITS EAR! I'LL SHOW THEM THAT THERE'S LIFE IN THE VULTURE YET!

AND NO ONE'S GOING TO STOP ME...NOT EVEN THAT INFERNAL SPIDER-MAN!

9

BUT, WHILE THE SEPTUAGENARIAN MASTER CRIMINAL SOARS ACROSS THE NEW YORK SKIES, HIS GREATEST NEMESIS HAS SWITCHED TO STREET CLOTHES AND MADE HIS WAY HERE...

...TO THE 17TH FLOOR OF THE DAILY BUGLE BUILDING--

--TO MAKE USE OF A WELL-STOCKED DARKROOM!

NOT BAD! THAT NEW LENS I BOUGHT HAS REALLY COME THROUGH FOR ME!

THESE ARE SOME OF THE BEST CRIME PHOTOS I'VE EVER TAKEN...SHARP AND CLEAR AS A BELL!

I CAN FEEL THE MONEY IN MY POCKET NOW!

BUT, IN THE NEXT INSTANT...

WHA--?! MY PICTURES ...THEY'RE RUINED!

BLAST IT, WHAT IGNORAMUS OPENED THE DOOR?!

WOULD YOU CARE TO REPHRASE THAT QUESTION, PARKER? I'M NOT KEEN ON HAVING FREELANCE EMPLOYEES CALL ME BY NAMES LESS RESPECTFUL THAN "SIR"!

RIGHT, BANNON?

YES, SIR, MR. JAMESON!

JONAH? I...UH....THAT IS...

DARN IT! ISN'T IT STILL CUSTOMARY--AT THIS NEWSPAPER--TO KEEP THE DARKROOM DOOR SHUT WHEN THE WARNING LIGHT TELLS YOU THAT SOMEONE'S DEVELOPING PICTURES... SIR?

WARNING LIGHT? WHAT WARNING LIGHT, PARKER?

THE BOSS-MAN IS RIGHT, PETEY...IT'S NOT LIT. ARE YOU SURE YOU FLIPPED THE DOOR SWITCH?

WAIT...I KNOW WHAT THE PROBLEM IS!

PLINK--

AH-HA! THERE'S A SHORT IN THE LIGHT! GEE, BAD BREAK, PETEY!

⑩

56

57

BE CAREFUL, HE SAYS... MINE OWN BROTHER! ISSAC, HAVEN'T THE TWO OF US BEEN IN THE TRADE ALL OUR LIVES?

YES, BUT--!

IN ALL THAT TIME, HAVE YOU EVER KNOWN ME *NOT* TO BE CAREFUL?

NO, BUT--!

THEN WOULD YOU PLEASE TO BE SHUTTING UP! LET ME PUT OUR NEW PURCHASES AWAY IN PEACE!

FORGIVE ME, MOSHEH! YOU KNOW HOW NERVOUS I GET!

THAT'S NO REASON TO BE...A... NOODGE.

OY GEVALT! ISSAC... LOOK!

GOOD AFTERNOON, GENTLEMEN! PLEASE WITHDRAW THAT TRAY FROM THE SAFE--VERY SLOWLY-- AND YOU'LL LIVE TO MAKE MANY MORE SUCH PURCHASES!

NOW THEN, BRING IT OVER HERE!

TERRIFIED, THE STEIN BROTHERS COMPLY WITH THE VULTURE'S DEMAND. AND THEN--

--BEFORE EITHER OF THEM CAN SO MUCH AS BLINK, THE WINGED MAN IS GONE!

⑫

IN THE DAYS THAT FOLLOW, THE VULTURE GOES ON A DARING ONE-MAN CRIME SPREE! NOTHING CAN WITHSTAND HIS BRAZEN ATTACKS...

...NOT ARMORED CARS...

...NOT BANKS...

...NOT EVEN THE MANHATTAN GOLD EXCHANGE!

AND WHERE IS SPIDER-MAN DURING THIS REIGN OF TERROR?

BROTHER, I AM AT A LOSS!

I WAS SURE THE VULTURE WOULD COME AFTER *ME!* OUR LAST LITTLE RUN-IN PUT HIM IN THE HOSPITAL... AND HE'S ALWAYS BEEN BIG ON REVENGE!

BUT HE ONLY SEEMS INTERESTED IN THEFT! HE'S BEEN STRIKING WHILE I'VE BEEN STUCK AT THE UNIVERSITY! THIS IS THE FIRST CHANCE I'VE HAD TO LOOK FOR HIM... AND IT'S RAINING!

HEY, THIS HAS ALL THE EAR-MARKS OF A VULTURE JOB! I MUST HAVE JUST MISSED HIM!

MAYBE I CAN PICK UP HIS TRAIL!

BUT THE VULTURE IS ALREADY MILES AWAY, ESCAPING WITH STILL MORE STOLEN BOOTY!

HELP, POLICE! HE CLEANED OUT MY STORE... STOLE MY MOST PRECIOUS GEMS!

13

MEANWHILE, IN THE MIDDLE OF A FRUITLESS SEARCH, A VERY SOGGY SPIDER-MAN IS COMING TO A CONCLUSION...

THIS IS FOR THE BIRDS!

ALL I'VE GOTTEN FOR MY TROUBLES IS SOAKED TO THE SKIN... AND THE MAKINGS OF A BRUTAL HEAD COLD!

THIS WEATHER IS MURDER ON MY SINUSES!

I'VE BEEN BOPPING BACK AND FORTH ACROSS MID-TOWN FOR HOURS, AND I HAVEN'T SEEN SO MUCH AS A PIGEON...TO SAY NOTHING OF THE VULTURE!

I MIGHT AS WELL GIVE UP THE SEARCH FOR NOW, AND HEAD HOME. I HAVE JUST ENOUGH TIME FOR A NICE HOT SHOWER, BEFORE I PICK UP AUNT MAY AND NATHAN FOR DINNER!

AND SO, ONE HOUR AND A VERY LONG BUS RIDE LATER...

IT'S A FUNNY THING ...RESTWELL NURSING HOME IS ONE OF THE BEST PUBLIC FACILI-TIES AROUND, BUT I STILL WISH AUNT MAY DIDN'T HAVE TO LIVE HERE.

IT'S SO STERILE!

BUT IT DOES NO GOOD TO WORRY, I CAN'T AFFORD ANY BETTER FOR HER...AND SHE DOES SEEM HAPPY HERE.

EXCUSE ME, MISS...ARE YOU ONE OF THE FINALISTS IN THE MISS UNIVERSE PAGEANT... OR LAST YEAR'S WINNER?

EH?

Woma

OH, PETER! I'M SO GLAD TO SEE YOU! THE WEATHER WAS SO BAD, I THOUGHT YOU MIGHT NOT MAKE IT!

HEY, A LITTLE RAIN ISN'T GOING TO KEEP ME FROM HAVING A NIGHT ON THE TOWN WITH MY FAVORITE AUNT AND HER BOYFRIEND!

SPEAKING OF NATHAN, WHERE IS HE?

HE'S STILL IN THE REC ROOM, PLAYING POKER WITH HIS CRONIES! SOMETIMES, I THINK THAT MAN WAS BORN ON A POKER TABLE!

WHY DON'T YOU GO GET HIM, WHILE I COLLECT MY THINGS?

THE "REC ROOM," EH? SURE THING, AUNT MAY!

THAT'S ANOTHER THING I DON'T LIKE ABOUT THIS PLACE... IT REMINDS ME TOO MUCH OF A HIGH SCHOOL!

AND NO ONE SHOULD HAVE TO LIVE IN SOMETHING LIKE THAT! HELLO, NATE!

HIYA, PETE! COME OVER HERE, I WANT YOU TO MEET A NEW BUDDY OF MINE!

TANK YOU, BOYS! AND NOW, HERE'S BOBBY AND CISSY WITH A SALUTE TO IOWA!

ADE, THIS YOUNG BUCK IS MAY'S NEPHEW PETER! HE'S A REAL GO-GETTER-- NOT ONLY GOES TO SCHOOL AT E.S.U.--

--BUT TAKES PICTURES FOR THE DAILY BUGLE IN HIS SPARE TIME!

UH,... I FOLD.

WHAT THE--?! MY SPIDER-SENSE IS TINGLING,... AND THE BUZZ IS GETTING STRONGER!

BUT WHAT DANGER COULD THERE BE HERE?

PETE, THIS FELLOW WITH THE BAD POKER HAND IS ADRIAN TOOMES!

PLEASED TO MEET... ...YOU.

A PHOTOGRAPHER! AND FROM THE LOOK ON HIS FACE, HE MUST HAVE RECOGNIZED ME!

I DON'T BELIEVE IT! I SPEND ALL DAY LOOKING FOR THE VULTURE, AND HE'S *HERE*?! IN MY AUNT'S NURSING HOME?!

EH...PUT 'ER THERE, YOUNG FELLA!

SO, YOU'RE A PHOTO-BUG ARE YOU? I DABBLE IN PHOTOGRAPHY MYSELF!

EVEN OUT OF COSTUME, HE'S AS STRONG AS EVER! THAT GRIP WOULD BE PAINFUL TO A NORMAL MAN!

WOULD YOU LIKE TO TAKE A LOOK AT MY SNAPSHOTS, SON?

OR WOULD YOU RATHER I REARRANGED YOUR INNARDS WITH THIS PISTOL?

NOW WHAT DO I DO?

I COULD DISARM THE VULTURE EASILY ENOUGH, BUT NATHAN AND THE OTHERS MIGHT BE HURT IN THE PROCESS.

GO ON WITH ADE, IF YOU WANT, PETE! I'M ON A ROLL RIGHT NOW... HAVEN'T BEEN DEALT HANDS LIKE THESE IN YEARS!

AH... ALL RIGHT, NATE!

WE WON'T BE GONE TOO LONG!

SECONDS LATER...

THAT'S IT-- THE DOOR JUST AHEAD!

YOU CAN'T HIDE HERE FOREVER, VULTURE! SOONER OR LATER, SOMEONE ELSE WILL RECOGNIZE YOU LIKE I DID!

THAT MAY WELL BE, YOUNGSTER! BUT FOR THE TIME BEING, THIS PLACE IS SERVING ME JUST FINE!

AND YOU'RE NOT GOING TO MESS THINGS UP!

WUNK

BLASTED YOUNG PUNKS! YOU'RE ALL ALIKE-- YOU ALL THINK I'M TOO OLD!

WELL, I'M MORE THAN ABLE TO HANDLE THE LIKES OF YOU!

17

63

THAT'S ALWAYS BEEN MY ACE-IN-THE-HOLE! NO ONE EXPECTS AN OLD MAN TO BE AS STRONG AS I!

I'M NO ORDINARY MAN! THEY ALMOST MADE ME FORGET THAT IN THE HOSPITAL! BUT NATHAN SNAPPED ME BACK TO NORMAL!

AND HERE AT RESTWELL, I HAVE THE PERFECT COVER!

NO ONE THINKS TO LOOK FOR THE VULTURE IN A NURSING HOME!

WHY, I WAS EVEN ABLE TO USE MY REAL NAME! NO ONE BOTHERED TO CHECK IT! NOW, MY YOUNG FRIEND... WE'LL SEE HOW WELL YOU FALL FROM TEN THOUSAND FEET.

NOK NOK

EH? WHO COULD THAT BE?

MR. TOOMES, NATHAN SAID THAT PETER CAME HERE WITH YOU.

WELL, HE DID, MRS. PARKER-- BUT HE DIDN'T STAY LONG!

HE SAID THAT HE HAD SOMETHING TO DO, AND HIGHTAILED IT OUT OF HERE.

I HOPE YOU'LL EXCUSE ME NOW, I WAS ABOUT TO TAKE A NAP!

OH, YES, OF COURSE.

WHAT COULD HAVE BEEN SO IMPORTANT THAT PETER WOULD LEAVE WITHOUT TELLING ME? HE HASN'T BEEN THAT THOUGHTLESS SINCE NATHAN WAS IN DANGER A MONTH AGO!

I THOUGHT THAT HE'D BECOME MORE RESPONSIBLE. HOW COULD I HAVE BEEN SO WRONG?

ALL RIGHT, PARKER, NOW--! EH?

LIKE YOU SAID, CHROME-DOME--

--THE MAN HAD SOMETHING IMPORTANT TO DO! BUT, IF YOU'RE WILLING, I'LL STAND IN FOR HIM!

SPIDER-MAN!! HOW--?

18

DING BUST IT, ADE-- *LET GO OF ME!* YOU WANT A FIGHT? I'LL GIVE YA ONE, YOU CRAZY WOOD'S COLT!

EH? N-NATHAN?

I DIDN'T KNOW THAT I'D GRABBED *YOU!* I JUST REACHED FOR THE CLOSEST WARM BODY.

YOU...GAVE ME MY LIFE BACK. HOW CAN I HURT YOU?

WHAT'S ALL THIS COMMOTION ABOUT? OH, MERCIFUL HEAVENS!

NATHAN!!

AS MAY PARKER'S SCREAM ECHOES THROUGH THE CHAMBER, EVERYTHING COMES TO A HALT! FOR A SECOND, NO ONE DARES EVEN BREATHE! AND THEN...

HERE!

WHOA!

RELAX, SIR! I HAVE YOU!

THE VULTURE COULD HAVE KILLED NATHAN...*WOULD* HAVE, IF HE HADN'T REALIZED WHO HE HAD! THERE MUST BE SOME HUMANITY LEFT IN THE OLD BIRD, AFTER ALL!

BUT, WHILE THE MASKED ADVENTURER HAS HIS HANDS FULL...

KRESH

THERE WILL BE OTHER BATTLES, SPIDER-MAN! THIS ISN'T OVER YET!

THEN...

YOU-- YOU SAVED US FROM THAT MADMAN!

FOLKS, PLEASE! LET ME THROUGH!

LEMME SHAKE YOUR HAND, MISTER! I ALWAYS KNEW THOSE EDITORIALS ABOUT YOU IN THE BUGLE WERE A LOT OF HOOEY!

21

AND SO, BY THE TIME SPIDER-MAN HAS MANAGED TO GENTLY GET AWAY FROM THE CROWD OF ELDERLY WELL-WISHERS...

GONE! MY LUCK IS STILL HOLDING...

...AND IT'S ALL BAD.

I'D BETTER CHANGE BACK TO MY CIVVIES, BEFORE AUNT MAY STARTS TO WORRY ABOUT HER NEPHEW.

BUT, AT THAT MOMENT, THERE'S JUST ONE MAN ON MAY PARKER'S MIND...

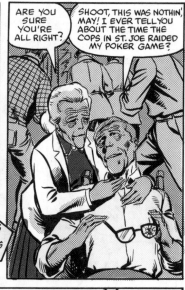

ARE YOU SURE YOU'RE ALL RIGHT?

SHOOT, THIS WAS NOTHIN', MAY! I EVER TELL YOU ABOUT THE TIME THE COPS IN ST. JOE RAIDED MY POKER GAME?

IT LOOKS LIKE I MISSED ALL THE EXCITEMENT!

WHY, PETER! YOU CAME BACK!

I WASN'T REALLY GONE. THE VULTURE TIED ME UP, BUT SPIDER-MAN FREED ME!

OH, YOU POOR BOY!

AW, I'M OKAY! HAS ANYONE CALLED THE POLICE?

OH! I GUESS I'D BETTER DO THAT!

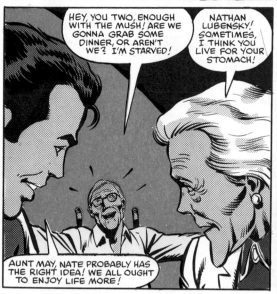

HEY, YOU TWO, ENOUGH WITH THE MUSH! ARE WE GONNA GRAB SOME DINNER, OR AREN'T WE? I'M STARVED!

NATHAN LUBENSKY! SOMETIMES, I THINK YOU LIVE FOR YOUR STOMACH!

AUNT MAY, NATE PROBABLY HAS THE RIGHT IDEA! WE ALL OUGHT TO ENJOY LIFE MORE!

WE NEVER KNOW WHEN SOMEONE LIKE THE VULTURE COULD COME ALONG AND PUT AN END TO IT!

THE END

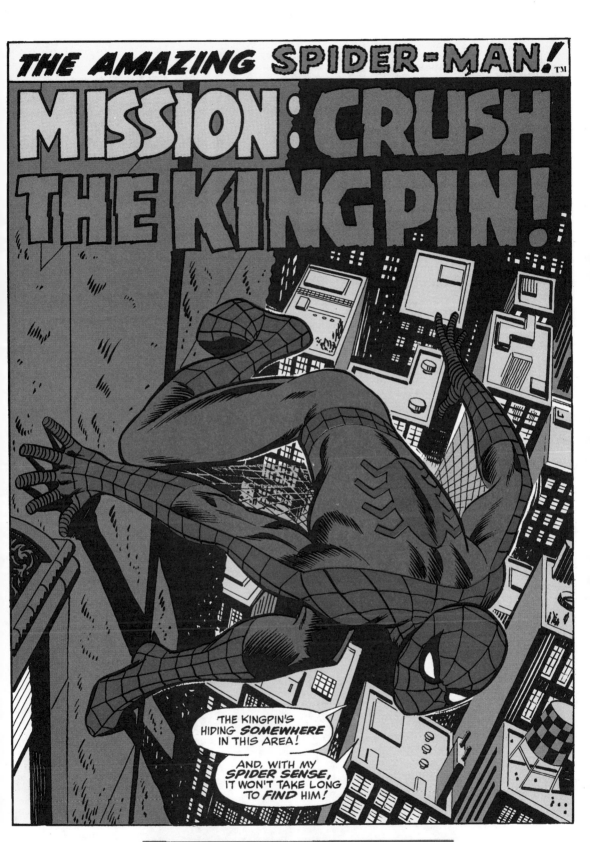

I *CAN'T* LET HIM GET AWAY WITH STEALING THAT PRICELESS *TABLET* FROM THE CAMPUS' *EXHIBITION HALL!*

...ESPECIALLY SINCE MR. ROBERTSON'S SON, *RANDY,* AND THE OTHER PROTEST LEADERS...

...ARE BEING *BOOKED* ON CHARGES OF *AIDING* THE KINGPIN IN HIS THEFT!

NOT TO MENTION THE FACT THAT THE TABLET IS SO *PRICELESS,* THAT FATSO CAN *SELL* IT TO ANY NATION HE CHOOSES!

UH-OH! SPIDEY SENSE IS STARTING TO *TINGLE!*

I'M GETTING *CLOSE!*

AND, JUST A FEW FATEFUL YARDS AWAY, WE FIND...

YOU *DID* IT, KINGPIN! IT WAS A STROKE OF *GENIUS* FOR YOU TO USE THE STUDENT *PROTEST DEMONSTRATION* AS A *COVER* FOR STEALING THE *TABLET!*

BUT WHAT ABOUT *SPIDER-MAN,* BOSS?

COULD YOU EXPECT ANY *LESS*...FROM *ME?*

YEAH! THE BLASTED *WEB-SPINNER* IS STILL ON OUR TRAIL!

FORGET SPIDER-MAN! LOOK AT THE *PRIZE* I'VE WON!

THIS ANCIENT *CLAY TABLET* IS OLDER THAN THE *DEAD SEA SCROLLS!*

WHOEVER *DECIPHERS* IT WILL LEARN THE GREATEST *SECRETS* OF ALL TIME!

AND IT'S *MINE! MINE!*

71

WHAT ABOUT *SPIDER-MAN*, RANDY? WHERE DOES *HE* FIT INTO ALL OF THIS?

I *TOLD* YOU, DAD! HE FOUGHT THE *KINGPIN*! HE SAVED MY *LIFE*!

OKAY, THEN! LETS GET BACK TO *YOU*...!

HOW'D YOU GET *MIXED-UP* IN THIS WHOLE THING?

I DID WHAT I THOUGHT WAS *RIGHT*, DAD...LIKE YOU ALWAYS *SAID* I SHOULD!

WE WANT THE HALL CONVERTED TO A *LOW-RENT DORM*...FOR NEEDY STUDENTS!

BUT THE DEAN WOULDN'T *LISTEN* TO US!

A *PROTEST* IS *ONE* THING!

BUT, THE *DAMAGE* YOU CAUSED..!

BUT DON'T *WORRY*, SON! YOUR MOM AND I WILL STAND *BEHIND* YOU!

WE WON'T LET YOU *DOWN*...WHEN YOU *NEED* US!

I JUST HAVE TO FIGURE OUT ...HOW TO *BREAK* IT TO HER!

YOU'RE TALKING...AS THOUGH I DID ...SOMETHING *AWFUL*!

DON'T YOU *SEE*? CAN'T YOU EVEN *UNDERSTAND*? I *HAVE* TO BE TOUGHER...I *HAVE* TO BE MORE MILITANT ---BECAUSE OF *YOU*!

YOU'VE BECOME PART OF THE *ESTABLISHMENT*... THE *WHITE MAN'S* ESTABLISHMENT!

I'VE GOTTA LIVE THAT *DOWN*!

BUT ISN'T THIS WHAT WE ALL *WANT*... WHAT WE'RE ALL *FIGHTING* FOR, BOY?

TO *MAKE* IT ON OUR *OWN*? TO PROVE WE'RE AS *GOOD*... OR *BETTER*---THAN ANY-ONE??

I DUNNO! I DUNNO *WHAT* TO THINK!

LOOK, MAN...*MAYBE* YOU'RE AN OKAY CAT... BUT WE GOTTA DO THINGS *OUR* WAY!

WE AIN'T NEVER GONNA GET *NOWHERE*... UNTIL WE KINDA SHAKE WHITEY *UP* A LITTLE!

HOW'S A MAN TO KNOW... WHAT'S *RIGHT*?

I WISH... I COULD *ANSWER* THAT, SON!

LISTEN! SOMETHING'S GOING *ON*... OUTSIDE!

COOK AN EGG... COOK YOUR GOOSE! TURN THE DEMONSTRATORS LOOSE!

GOWAN *HOME,* KIDS! THE PARTY'S *OVER*!

C'MON, BREAK IT UP...*BREAK IT UP*!

5

THIS WON'T HELP! YOU'RE ALL MAKING THINGS WORSE!

GETTING OURSELVES ARRESTED WON'T GIVE US THE LOW-RENT DORM WE NEED!

OKAY, BEAUTIFUL! GOT ANY BETTER IDEAS?

HEY! IT'S GWEN STACY!

WHERE'S YOUR CHICKEN BOY FRIEND, LADY?

LET OUR LEADERS GO

HE HASN'T THE GUTS TO TAKE A STAND WITH US!

YOU SAID PETER PARKER DOESN'T HAVE GUTS?!!

YEAH...IT'S PARKER I'M TALKIN' ABOUT!

...AND YOU BETTER BELIEVE IT!

YOU CRUMMY, DIM-WITTED LOUDMOUTH!

HE COULD BE HALF THE MAN HE IS...

AND STILL MAKE TEN OF YOU!

SAY, TAKE IT EASY, LITTLE GIRL! YOU DON'T WANNA BE ACCUSED OF CIVILIAN BRUTALITY!

POLICE

OH, GWEN STACY! I DIDN'T RECOGNIZE YOU!

I'M GOING IN...TO SEE MY FATHER!

GWEN! I DIDN'T THINK YOU'D BE HERE!

WHY NOT? I MAY BE YOUR DAUGH-TER...BUT I'M STILL A CO-ED AT E.S.U.!

WHOA THERE, YOUNG LADY! WHAT'S GOT YOU ALL STEAMED UP?

JUST SOME FEATHER-BRAINED LUNKHEAD OUTSIDE!

DID HE GET FRESH WITH YOU?

HIM? HE WOULDN'T DARE!

NO...HE SAID SOME ROTTEN THINGS...ABOUT PETER!

ARE YOU UPSET... BECAUSE YOU THINK THEY MAY BE TRUE?

I...WISH I KNEW!

6

81

84

IF HE WAS TRYING TO *ESCAPE*... HE'D BE GOING THE *OTHER* WAY!

BUT, HE'S *NOT*...WHICH JUST MIGHT MEAN *ONE* THING...

HE *COULD* BE AFTER THE STOLEN *TABLET*!

THE KINGPIN'LL HAVE TO *KEEP*!

RIGHT *NOW*, THE TABLET IS *MORE* IMPORTANT!

WHILE OUTSIDE, AT THAT MOMENT...

THAT'S *RIGHT*, SARGE! I SPOTTED THE KINGPIN'S *CAR* OVER THERE...

AND THEN I HEARD A *SHOT*---FROM INSIDE THE BUILDING!

ALL RIGHT, MEN! WHAT ARE WE *WAITING* FOR?

THERE HE *IS*! WE *FOUND* 'IM!

QUICK! GET THE *CUFFS* ON HIM WHILE HE'S STILL *GROGGY*!

THE *POLICE*! ...THEY'LL *NEVER* BE ABLE TO *HOLD* ME!

BUT I WON'T YET *RESIST*! I'VE SOMETHING THAT MUST BE *DONE* FIRST...!

WHERE'S THE *TABLET*, KINGPIN? WE *KNOW* YOU'VE GOT IT!

DO YOU THINK I'D *KEEP* IT HERE...WHERE IT COULD *INCRIMINATE* ME?

UNTIL YOU *FIND* IT, YOU'LL *NEVER* BE ABLE TO PROVE MY *GUILT*!

AND, BY *NOW*, MY WEB-SWINGING *ALLY* HAS TAKEN IT SAFELY *AWAY* FROM HERE!

...JUST AS HE WILL FREE *ME* FROM CAPTIVITY---WHEN THE TIME IS *RIPE*!

THEN JAMESON WAS *RIGHT*! SPIDER-MAN'S IN THIS AS DEEP AS *YOU*!

WITH A FEW CHOICE *WORDS*, I'VE SEALED THE WALL-CRAWLER'S *DOOM*!

MEANWHILE, *UNAWARE* OF HOW DEEPLY HE'S BEEN *IMPLICATED*, SPIDEY CONTINUES TO DO HIS THING...

NO ONE CAN OPEN IT THE WAY THE *KINGPIN* COULD---

BUT, IF I CAN FIND MYSELF ENOUGH *EX-PLOSIVES*..!!

DON'T *BOTHER*, *BRIGHT BOY!*

WHO..??!

THERE! THAT'LL KEEP YOU ALL COMFY-COZY!

NO *WONDER* NO ONE CAN OPEN THIS THING...

THERE'S NO *LOCK* TO JIMMY! NO COMBINATION! *NOTHING!*

THIS!!

WHICH MEANS THAT TUBBY MUST HAVE USED *RAW STRENGTH!*

JUST *EXACTLY* LIKE...

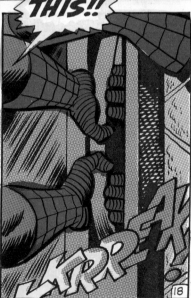

18

AND *NOW*... IF MY HUNCH WAS *RIGHT*... YEP! THERE IT *IS*!

IT'S HARD TO *BELIEVE* THAT THIS PETRIFIED *STONE* IS ONE OF THE MOST *VALUABLE* OBJECTS ON EARTH!

I WONDER IF THEY'LL *EVER* LEARN WHAT THESE HIERO-GLYPHICS *MEAN*?

WAIT! YOU CAN'T *LEAVE* ME HERE!

DON'T *BET* ON IT, MISTER!

THE *COPS*'LL PICK HIM UP BEFORE HE GETS TOO *LONELY*!

THEN, SECONDS LATER, AFTER FINDING THE KINGPIN *GONE*---

WOW! THE BLUECOATS HAVE LANDED *ALREADY*!

DIDN'T TAKE THEM *LONG* TO MAKE THE SCENE!

NOW I WON'T HAVE TO CARRY THE *TABLET* ALL OVER TOWN!

HOLD IT, GANG! I'VE *GOT* SOMETHING FOR YOU!

IT'S SPIDER-MAN!

HE'S OUT TO FREE THE *KINGPIN*!

WATCH IT! HE'S GONNA *TOSS* SOMETHING AT US!

THEY'RE *FIRING* AT ME!!

GIVE YOURSELF *UP*...OR OUR NEXT SHOT WON'T *MISS*!

19.

87

IF YOU CHOOSE TO *SHOOT* ME, DO IT WHILE MY BACK IS *TURNED*. IT'S THE *ONLY* CHANCE YOU'LL GET.

BUT ASK YOURSELF "*WHAT IF I MISS?*"

HAH HAH HAH

NOW, ARRANGER, I WOULD HAVE WORDS WITH YOU.

I EXPECTED AS MUCH.

I AM THE BEST *ASSASSIN* IN TOWN AND I HAVEN'T RECEIVED AN ASSIGNMENT IN MONTHS!

I WANT TO KNOW WHY THE KINGPIN HAS *BLACK-LISTED* ME!

ISN'T IT *OBVIOUS?*

NO, I WOULD GUESS NOT.

MY DEAR MACENDALE-- YOU ARE A *BOOR!*

WHAT?!

YOU ARE AN *IDIOT.* AN *INCOMPETENT.* A *PRATTLING FOOL.* YOU *STEAL ANOTHER MAN'S IDENTITY* AND YOU EXPECT TO BE RESPECTED FOR THAT?

ABSURD.

I NEVER TOOK YOU FOR THE *SUICIDAL TYPE,* ARRANGER!

YOU ARE TRULY *HOPELESS.*

THEN AGAIN... PERHAPS THERE *IS* A CHANCE FOR YOU YET...

HOW?

A TEST-- TO PROVE YOU ARE *WORTHY* OF THE HOBGOBLIN PERSONA...

PERHAPS IF YOU WERE ABLE TO *ELIMINATE* SOMEONE WHO HAS BEEN AN *OBSTACLE* FOR THE KINGPIN...

SOMEONE LIKE... *SPIDER-MAN?*

YES! YESSS!! IT WOULD BE A *PLEASURE* TO DESTROY THAT *PEST!*

I WILL *BLEED* HIM LIKE A *SPONGE* AND DROP HIS *CARCASS* ON YOUR DESK!

NO NEED TO BE SO *EXTREME*, THOUGH I UNDERSTAND THE SENTIMENT.

NOW THEN, IF THAT'S SETTLED...

SWISH

HUH?

I'D LIKE TO INTRODUCE YOU TO THE ORGANIZATION'S *NEWEST* EMPLOYEE.

HIS NAME IS *TOMBSTONE*. HE IS GOOD AT DISCARDING WASTE.

WHAT ARE YOU--

AND I DO SO ENJOY DISCARDING WASTE...

AAAAAAGH!

AAAAAA!!

HOW COULD HE--?!

GOT TO CALM DOWN.

MY CYBERNETIC REMOTE CONTROL!

KICK IT IN NOW--

HEY-- WHAT'D YOU DO?!

I DIDN'T TOUCH IT!

VVVRROOOM

CRASH.

AGH!

HMMM.

REMOTE CONTROL GUIDANCE. CYBERNETIC LINK, I'D IMAGINE. HARD TO CALL IT UP MECHANICALLY WHILE YOU ARE FLAILING LIKE A CHICKEN.

SMOOTH.

MADE IT! JUST BARELY.

I'LL KILL SPIDER-MAN FOR YOU, ARRANGER--

--THEN I'LL KILL YOU FOR MYSELF!

FASCINATING. PERHAPS HE'LL SUCCEED?

DON'T BE AFRAID.

NONSENSE. I WAS CONSIDERING HIS CHANCE OF ERADICATING THAT WALL-CRAWLING IRRITANT!

DOWNTOWN AT 410 CHELSEA STREET, ANOTHER TYPE OF MENACE IS ALSO ON THE PROWL...

WHERE DID YOU GO?!

:HUMFF:

WHERE ARE YOU, YOU NO GOOD LAZY--

IT'S BEEN OVER AN *HOUR* SINCE HE WENT TO CHECK THE BOILER! WHERE COULD HE HAVE GONE OFF TO?

NOISE?

COMING FROM UPSTAIRS... LEADING TO...

OF COURSE. OUT OF ALL MY TENANTS, I CAN ALWAYS COUNT ON TROUBLE FROM...

...PARKER!!!

ULP!

YOU THINK RANDI'S GOING TO GIVE HIM A *HEART ATTACK*?

DID I EVER TELL YOU ABOUT MY CHARLESTON DAYS?

THIS BIG, I'M NOT KIDDING, *JOY!*

HOW MUCH DID IT COST YOU, *LANCE?*

I'M MUCH BETTER NOW, GLORY, THANK YOU.

-- DON'T KNOW, *MRS. WATSON,* BUT HE'S A REAL *PARTY ANIMAL!*

OH, *FLASH!*

JONAH, SURPRISED TO SEE YOU HERE.

ROBBIE, YOU WOUND ME! PETER IS *MORE* THAN AN *EMPLOYEE,* I THINK OF HIM AS A *SON.*

A *NAGEL* ON THE WALL. BUT OF COURSE.

95

MRS. MUGGINS! TO WHAT DO WE OWE THE PLEASURE?

UH... I'M LOOKING FOR SOMEONE...

MOST OF THE FREE WORLD'S HERE! C'MON IN AND JOIN THE PARTY!!

BUT, JONAH, IF YOU THINK SO HIGHLY OF HIM, WHY DON'T YOU PAY HIM BETTER?

BECAUSE RELATIVES WORK CHEAP, MARTHA.

IT'S THAT BIG, I'M SERIOUS!

GIRLS, LET'S PLAY A LITTLE GAME OF HIDE AND GO SEEK!

WHAT ARE WE HIDING FROM?

A PAINFUL BEATING!

MINDY! AHA! HELP ME FIND A HIDING PLACE!

LISTEN, BUSTER, THE ONLY THING HIDING HERE IS A RIGHT HOOK THAT MAKES TYSON WORRY!

HMMM...

HMMM... WHO OR WHAT IS THAT?

PETER'S LANDLADY. STAY CLEAR OF HER IF YOU VALUE YOUR LIFE.

MJ-- WHERE'S THE HARRIED HUBBY?

IN THE KITCHEN GETTING THE FOOD READY.

IN THE KITCHEN, EH?

PETER-- NEED A HAND WITH ANYTHING?

NO THANKS, HON. THE MUNCHIES ARE READY!

HORS D'OEUVRES, MR. PARKER.

RIGHT. SILLY ME.

OH, TIGER, I KNOW YOU'RE NOT BIG ON PARTYING LIKE I AM, BUT YOU'RE A SWEETIE FOR LETTING ME GET AWAY WITH THIS!

IT'LL BE FUN...

97

MJ, THIS COULD BE TAKEN AS GROUNDS FOR A DIVORCE! I STILL OWE LAST MONTH'S RENT! AND I DON'T HAVE ANY MONEY TO PAY HER! CAN'T EXPECT MJ TO KEEP BAILING ME OUT! HIDING'S MY BEST BET!

OH, PETEY, DAHLING...

I'M JASMINE. MJ'S TOLD US SOOO MUCH ABOUT YOU. WE JUST HAVE TO CHIT-CHAT!

BUT OF COURSE, PETER.

UHM... YEAH. BEEN DOING A LITTLE SUB-STITUTE TEACHING ON THE SIDE.

UH... SURE. YOU ALL WORK WITH MJ?

ARE YOU STILL A PHOTOGRAPHER?

SHE'S PARKED BY THE PUNCH... WONDER WHERE RANDI, CANDI, AND BAMBI ARE...

OH PUBLIC SCHOOLS ARE SIMPLY BRUTAL! HAVE YOU BEEN ASSAULTED YET?

UM, YOU'D BE SURPRISED!

RING

SAVED BY THE BELL!

EXCUSE ME.

HELLO. AUNT MAY! HOW ARE YOU? NO, DON'T BE.

IT'S UH... INTERESTING.

I'M HANGING IN THERE. MARY JANE'S HAVING A BALL! YES, ANNA'S HERE, SURE I WILL, I LOVE YOU, TOO. TALK TO YOU SOON. BYE-BYE.

IRRESISTIBLE FORCE, MEET IMMOVABLE OBJECT.

ANOTHER WOMAN?

HEH-HEH. YOU COULD SAY THAT.

THAT'S A SHAME. I'D LOVE TO BE THE OTHER WOMAN. IN YOUR MARRIAGE.

EXCUSE ME?

I FIND YOUR SHY, AWKWARD SWEETNESS REFRESHING. MARY JANE NEED NEVER KNOW.

UHM... I BETTER GET OUT OF HERE.

BROTHER?! IS IT ME OR ARE MJ'S FRIENDS A LITTLE ODD?

GOOD PUNCH, THOUGH!

GREEN IS A HAIR COLOR TO ENVY, I ASSURE YOU...

98

PETEY! BAMBI, RANDI, CANDI, HAVING A GOOD TIME?

THE DOG WANTS TO PLAY THE PIANO?

IT'S A BLAST! BUT WE'RE GOING TO MISS YOU SO MUCH WHEN YOU MOVE OUT!

WE'LL NEVER GET A NEIGHBOR AS CUTE AS YOU ARE!

YEAH, WELL... I'LL VISIT, BUT I'M MARRIED NOW.

OH, YOU!

I WAS JUST SAYING HOW MARRIAGE IS AN INSTITUTION WHICH HAS CAST A PERFECTLY PALLID LIGHT ON GOOD TIMES!

SHALL WE DANCE?

TALK TO YOU LATER, PETE.

MISSING ME ALREADY, I CAN TELL.

" WHAT A NIGHT THIS IS TURNING INTO! "

WHERE AM I GOING TO FIND AN OPEN AREA TO STAGE MY ASSAULT ON THAT MISERABLE WALL-CRAWLER?

TIMES SQUARE? NO, TOO MANY BUILDINGS, TOO MANY HIDING PLACES--IT WOULD BE TO MY DISADVANTAGE.

THE *PORT AUTHORITY?* NO. SUBURBAN COMMUTERS WOULD MAKE *TANTALIZING BAIT*, BUT I WOULD HAVE NO ROOM TO MANEUVER...

PORT AUTHORITY BUS TERMINAL

SUBURBAN? YES! PERFECT!

"AFTER ALL THIS TIME. AFTER YEARS AS A *MERCENARY* IN THE DIRTIEST WARS ACROSS THE WORLD...

"AFTER COUNTLESS DEFEATS AS *JACK O'LANTERN*...

"I THOUGHT ACQUIRING THE *ORIGINAL* HOBGOBLIN'S CRIMINAL MATERIALS WOULD HAVE BEEN MY ANSWER...

"BUT WHEN I HAD SPIDER-MAN'S *DEFEAT* IN MY GRASP, A *CIVILIAN* STOPPED ME..."

NOW. *NOW IS MY TIME.* I AM PREPARED TO MAKE MY STAND. TO DEFEAT SPIDER-MAN AND *MOVE UP* IN THE CRIMINAL WORLD.

LINCOLN TUNNEL

AND I HAVE FOUND THE *PERFECT* STAGING GROUND TO BATTLE HIM!

100

HAY-LO! HARRY!! WHERE THE HECK ARE YOU MY FELLOW FRIEND IN WEDDED BLISS?!

WHERE?

WE'RE STUCK IN TRAFFIC OUTSIDE THE *LINCOLN TUNNEL*, PETE.

ACCORDING TO THE RADIO, THE *HOBGOBLIN* IS CAUSING SOME PROBLEMS ON THE NEW YORK SIDE.

LINCOLN TUNNEL
CARS PAY $3.00

YOU KNOW ABOUT THE TROUBLE I HAD WITH HIM IN THE PAST, I DON'T WANT TO TAKE ANY CHANCES.

UH-OH. HOBGOBLIN.

MJ'LL KILL ME IF I LEAVE THE PARTY!

THEN AGAIN, SO WILL HOBBY!

BUT, IT'S A GREAT CHANCE TO SNAP SOME *PIX* AND *PAY MY RENT!*

MJ, THERE'S AN *ITSY-BITSY PROBLEM.* COME INTO THE BATHROOM, PLEASE...

THIS MUSIC IS SO-- LOUD!

AMANDA AND RANDY SEEM TO BE ENJOYING IT.

WHAT'S WRONG?

HARRY CALLED, HE'S TIED UP IN TRAFFIC. HE SAID THE HOBGOBLIN IS CAUSING THE TROUBLE,

PETER! WHAT ABOUT THE PARTY?!

I'LL BE BACK IN A MINUTE. *TWO, TOPS. PROMISE.*

JUST COVER FOR ME, OKAY?

IS IT ALWAYS GOING TO BE LIKE THIS? DON'T KNOW WHETHER I WANT TO HUG HIM OR KICK HIM!

PETER, HAVE SOME PUNCH, LET'S TALK!

'S A DEAL, JOY, IF YOU LET ME DELAY THE CHIT-CHAT TILL AFTER I GO OUT AN' GET SOME-- WHAT AM I GETTING? SOME MUNCHIES, THA'S RIGHT!

SIX MINUTES LATER AND THIRTEEN BLOCKS UPTOWN...

WHERE ARE YOU, *SPIDER-MAN!* I WON'T STOP UNTIL YOU SHOW YOURSELF! I WANT *YOUR HEAD SERVED ON A PLATTER!*

HOWZ 'BOUT MY *FEET* IN YO' *FACE!*

KATACK!

AAAGHH!

YOUR *COWARDLY ATTACKS* WON'T HELP YOU WIN THIS BATTLE!

DEY COULDN' HURT!

MISSED AGAIN! ALMOST DIDN'T LAND RIGHT! WHAT IS *WRONG* WITH ME?!

DO NOT ENTER

HAHAHAHAHA!

HUH?

ARE YOU HAVING SOME *DIFFICULTIES*, YOU WALL-CRAWLING *SLIME?*

JUS' TOYIN' WIT' YA, *HOBBY!*

I'M IN B!!!!!!G TROUBLE!

104

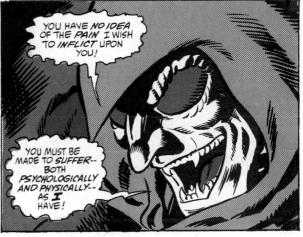

WELLLLL... YOU STILL HAVE YOUR LOOKS.

CONTINUE TO MOCK ME IF YOU--

EH?

HUH?

OH-OH.

CYBERNETIC CONTROL ISN'T WORKING!

THE *ELECTRICAL DISCHARGE* FROM THE LIGHT TOWER *EXPLOSION* MUST HAVE--

YAAAAAAA!

ARRIVEDERCI, DUMMY!

DO NOT ENTER THIS LANE

SHVVVRROOOM

WOW. HE'S GONNA RUN OUT OF GAS SOON!

MAYBE OVER THE *HUDSON RIVER.* OR BETTER YET, OVER *NEW JERSEY!*

THIS WAS A MESS! AT LEAST NO ONE GOT HURT.

JAMESON'S GONNA SNAP THESE PIX UP! "SPASTIC SPIDEY TIES UP TUNNEL TRAFFIC!" FIGURES THE BEST WAY TO *MAKE MONEY* IS BY COMPROMISING MYSELF!

ONCE I FIND OUT HOW I GOT THIS WAY I'LL MAKE SURE IT *NEVER* HAPPENS AGAIN!

GOTTA GET BACK TO THE *PARTY*-- CAN'T *SWING* HOME... *DON'T TRUST* MY REFLEXES.

THIS COULD TAKE A LITTLE WHILE...

109

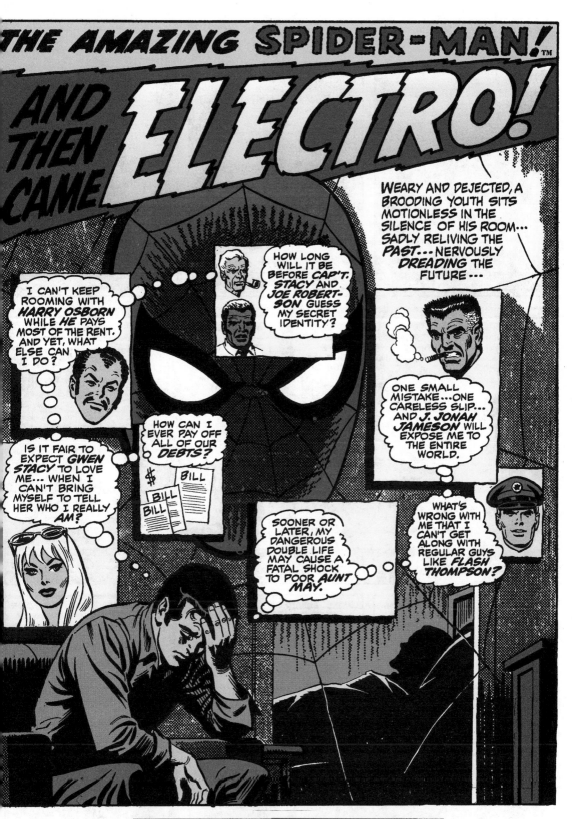

STAN LEE & JOHN ROMITA, SR.—Plot
STAN LEE—Script
JOHN ROMITA, SR.—Penciller
JIM MOONEY—Inker
SAM ROSEN—Letterer

NUTS! I'LL BE A CANDIDATE FOR A *SHRINKER* IF I KEEP *PITYING* MYSELF THIS WAY.

BETTER SNAP *OUT* OF IT. I COULDN'T EVEN *AFFORD* A PSYCHIATRIST.

MAN! DO I FEEL *DOWN.*

THE ONLY STROKE OF *LUCK* I'VE HAD LATELY WAS LAST NIGHT---

.. WHEN I CONVINCED AUNT MAY SHE ONLY *IMAGINED* SEEING THE *WEB DUMMY* I LEFT IN MY ROOM.

SO, I GOT MYSELF OFF THE *HOOK* BY MAKING HER THINK SHE WAS *SEEING* THINGS.

BY FORCING MY OWN *AUNT* TO START DOUBTING HER *SANITY.*

WHICH MAKES *ME* LOWER THAN---UH OH ---THE *BELL.*

RINNGG

MRS. WATSON--- AND *MARY JANE.* I-- I THOUGHT YOU WERE STILL IN *FLORIDA.*

AND WAS IT EVER A *GROOVE,* PETEY-O.

WE TOOK THE VERY FIRST *PLANE*---AS SOON AS I HEARD THAT MAY WAS *AILING* AGAIN!

NOW THAT *SHE'S* HERE TO LOOK AFTER AUNT MAY, I'LL BE ABLE TO GET BACK TO MY *OWN* PAD.

DON'T WORRY ABOUT A *THING,* PETER. I'LL SOON HAVE HER RIGHT AS RAIN.

HERE, P.P. ---*GWEN* WANTS YOU TO CALL HER.

HI, GWENDY. WHAT? THE FARE-WELL DINNER FOR *FLASH?* OH, I-- HAD ALMOST *FORGOTTEN.*

WE WON'T *LET* YOU FORGET, MAN. CAN'T HAVE THE *BASH,* 'LESS EVERYONE CHIPS IN.

WELL, LOVER--- I JUST WANTED TO *REMIND* YOU NOT TO SPEND YOUR EXTRA MONEY ON FRIVOLOUS THINGS LIKE *YACHTS* AND *CADILLACS!*

AND REMEMBER--- MJ IS *OFF-LIMITS* TO GWENDOLYN'S GUY.

I'VE GOTTA SCARE UP SOME BREAD FOR FLASH'S PARTY *SOMEHOW.*

SEE YOU *LATER,* LADY. I HAVE TO *RUN.*

MMMM--- I'D BETTER CHECK MY *MOUTH-WASH*

WOW, I'M *FLATTER* THAN JOLLY JONAH'S *TOP KNOT!*

THERE'S JUST *NO* WAY FOR PENNILESS PARKER TO RAISE THE *CASH* HE NEEDS FOR FLASH'S GOING-AWAY PARTY.

BUT, IT'S JUST *POSSIBLE* THAT MY WALL-CRAWLING *ALTER EGO* MAY HAVE A *BETTER* CHANCE.

ANYWAY, THERE'S NO HARM IN *TRYING.*

BUT, A HALF-HOUR LATER...

MY LUCK'S RUNNING TRUE TO FORM ...ALL *BAD.*

I HAVEN'T SPOTTED A SINGLE *CRIME* TO PHOTOGRAPH.

WHENEVER I NEED A *BAD GUY*...THE WHOLE WORLD'S *SIMON PURE.*

OH *NO!* WHO NEEDED THAT *CHIMNEY* TO SUDDENLY START *BELCHING?*

NOW I'M NOT ONLY THE *POOREST* WEB-HEAD AROUND... BUT THE *DIRTIEST.*

A TYPICAL FUN HOUR IN FUN CITY...AND ALL I'VE GOT TO *SHOW* FOR IT IS A GRIMY *COSTUME.*

IF ONLY I HAD TAKEN SOME PICTURES OF THE *KANGAROO* WHILE WE WERE FIGHTING...

BUT *LITTLE MARY SUNSHINE* OVER THERE ISN'T PAYING OFF FOR *IFS, ANDS* OR *BUTS.*

...SO JUST KEEP *SWINGIN'* ALONG, SPIDEY.

115

KEEP YOUR *SHIRTS* ON. ALL WE GOTTA DO IS THROW THIS *CIRCUIT BREAKER.*

STAY *AWAY* FROM THERE, DILLON---

THAT'S GOT ENOUGH *VOLTS* RUNNING THRU IT TO STOP AN *ARMY!*

DON'T DILLON! DON'T TOUCH IT!

YOU-- YOU *DID* IT! AND YOU'RE STILL *STANDING.* BUT *HOW,* DILLON--- *HOW?*

MAYBE IT'S 'CAUSE I'M WEARIN' *RUBBER SOLES.*

NO... IT'S *IMPOSSIBLE!* ALL OF THAT *CURRENT...*

SO WHY AIN'T I *DEAD?*

IT'S *ALL RIGHT* NOW, JB. I DON'T KNOW *HOW*--- BUT THAT NEW *ELECTRICIAN,* MAX DILLON, MANAGED TO FIX THE SHORT.

AWRIGHT, AWRIGHT. GIVE HIM A FIVE BUCK *RAISE...*

--AND GET EVERYONE BACK TO *WORK.*

MAX DILLON... I FEEL LIKE I'VE *HEARD* THAT NAME *BEFORE.*

FORGET IT, PAL. YOU'RE PROBABLY THINKING OF THE MARSHAL IN *GUNSMOKE.*

NOW C'MON--- WE'VE GOT SOME *BUSINESS* TO DISCUSS.

WAS IT MY *IMAGINATION...* OR DID MY *SPIDER-SENSE* TINGLE WHEN DILLON *LOOKED* AT ME?

FIRST THING YOU'LL NEED IS A GOOD *AGENT.*

NOW I'VE GOT A *BROTHER-IN-LAW...*

IF I KNEW *SPIDER-MAN* WAS HERE, I WOULD'A BEEN MORE *CAREFUL.*

BUT I DIDN'T THINK I HAD ANYTHING TO *WORRY* ABOUT FROM THOSE *OTHER* SLOBS!

ANYWAY, I HAD A *CHANCE* TO TEST MY *POWER* AGAIN.

BUT I *STILL* GOTTA LAY LOW A WHILE LONGER... TILL MY PLANS ARE *RIPE*...TILL *ELECTRO* IS READY TO *STRIKE* ONCE MORE.

AND THEN--- NOT EVEN *SPIDER-MAN*'LL BE ABLE TO *STOP* ME.

FOR THOSE OF YOU *NEW* TO THE ANNALS OF SPIDER-DOM, *ELECTRO* FIRST GAINED HIS UNCANNY POWER---

...WHEN MAX DILLON, AN ORDINARY *LINEMAN*, WAS STRUCK BY *LIGHTNING* WHILE REPAIRING SOME HIGH-TENSION ELECTRIC WIRES...

DUE TO A ONE-IN-A-BILLION SET OF CONDITIONS, THE ACCIDENT GAVE HIM TOTAL *MASTERY* OVER THE POWER OF ELECTRICITY...

...MASTERY ENOUGH TO DEFEAT OUR HERO DURING THEIR FIRST EPIC BATTLE---

IT WAS ONLY DUE TO ELECTRO'S OWN *OVER-CONFIDENCE* THAT SPIDEY WAS FINALLY ABLE TO TURN DEFEAT INTO VICTORY...

LATER, THE WEB-SPINNER SCORED ONCE AGAIN BY *GROUNDING* HIMSELF WITH A WIRE WHICH HE HASTILY ATTACHED TO HIS LEG.

THE *NEXT* TIME WE MEET, *ELECTRO* ISN'T GONNA MAKE ANY MISTAKES. *NEXT* TIME I'LL ...UH OH...

MY BLASTED *PAROLE OFFICER'S* WAITIN' FOR ME.

HELLO, DILLON.

YOU NEVER *FORGET,* DO YA?

JUST WANTED TO *TELL* YOU THAT I HEARD ABOUT YOUR *HEROISM* AT THE TV STUDIO.

IT'S A GOOD *BEGINNING,* DILLON. KEEP UP THE GOOD WORK---AND I'LL SEE YOU NEXT MONTH.

YEAH.. YEAH.. SURE. YOU *DO* THAT, MISTER.

SMUG PUNK. I'D LIKE TO WIPE THAT *SMILE* OFF HIS FACE.

BUT I GOTTA PLAY IT *COOL*...TILL THE TIME COMES.

WHEN I'M READY TO GO BACK INTO ACTION...AS *ELECTRO* AGAIN...*NOBODY'S* GONNA PUSH ME AROUND. *NOBODY!*

BZZIK!

THIS IS *J. JONAH JAMESON*, WITH THE DAILY BUGLE'S TV *EDITORIAL* FOR TONIGHT...

WE'VE JUST LEARNED THAT *SPIDER-MAN* WILL BE A GUEST ON THE *MIDNIGHT TALK SHOW*...

ON BEHALF OF THE *DECENT ELEMENT* IN THIS CITY...OR WHAT'S *LEFT* OF IT...MY NEWSPAPER *PROTESTS* THIS OUTRAGE!

WE MUST NOT ALLOW A LAWLESS, MASKED *CRIMINAL* TO BE GLAMORIZED AND PUBLICIZED ON FAMILY TV.

THAT PUBLIC ENEMY MUST BE *JAILED*...NOT *HAILED!*

YOU TELL 'EM, FLAT-HEAD.

HEY...*WAIT* A MINUTE. THIS MAY BE THE *CHANCE* ELECTRO'S BEEN *WAITIN'* FOR.

I'M BETTIN' THAT CREEP *JAMESON*'LL PAY A *BUNDLE* TO ANYONE WHO *UNMASKS* THE WEB-SPINNER RIGHT ON TV...WITH EVERYONE *WATCHIN'!*

AND THE GUY WHO *DOES* IT WON'T EVEN BE BREAKIN' THE *LAW.*

IT'LL BE TWO BIRDS WITH *ONE BOLT.*

I'LL BE *PAID* FOR GETTIN' MY REVENGE ON *SPIDER-MAN.*

118

SECONDS LATER...

IT'S BEEN A *LONG* TIME SINCE *ELECTRO* MOVED THRU TOWN BY HARNESSING THE POWER OF *ELECTRIC CABLES*...

BUT I'M AS *GOOD* AT IT NOW AS I *EVER* WAS.

MEANWHILE, A PENSIVE *PETER PARKER* MOVES ALONG AT HIS OWN PRAGMATIC PACE...

THEY WOULDN'T PAY ME IN *ADVANCE* FOR PROMISING TO APPEAR ON THEIR SHOW.

GUESS I CAN'T *BLAME* THEM. WHY SHOULD THEY *TRUST* SPIDEY?

BUT I'M *SICK* OF BEING SO *BROKE* ALL THE TIME. IF ONLY...

COMING *IN*, PETER... OR DO YOU JUST HAVE A THING ABOUT RINGING *DOORBELLS*?

OH... *HI*, GWEN.

SORRY, PRETTY GIRL. GUESS I WAS A LITTLE *PRE-OCCUPIED!*

THAT'S OKAY, MR. P. A GIRL CAN'T TAKE *TOO* MUCH OF ALL THIS FLAMING *PASSION*, ANYWAY!

HELLO, PETER. HAVE YOU HEARD THE NEWS ABOUT *SPIDER-MAN* BEING SCHEDULED FOR A TV APPEARANCE?

OUR FRIEND *JAMESON* IS HAVING *CONNIPTIONS* ABOUT IT!

SORRY, DAD. THIS SCINTILLATING LAD IS *MINE* TONIGHT!

HMMM... I *SUSPECTED* AS MUCH-

THE MOST *BEAUTIFUL* FEMALE IN TOWN... AND I CAN'T EVEN AFFORD TO TAKE HER IN A *TAXI*. NUTS!

REMEMBER, PETE... FLASH MUSTN'T *SUSPECT* THAT WE'RE PLANNING A *PARTY* FOR HIM.

WHAT'LL I *DO* WHEN I HAVE TO CHIP IN?

THERE *MUST* BE A WAY TO... *UH OH!* HOPE GWEN DIDN'T NOTICE I CRACKED THE *PORCELAIN*.

FINALLY, AT THE EVER-POPULAR *COFFEE BEAN*...

HI, GWENDY. COULDN'T GET A *DATE* TONIGHT, HUH?

COME *OFF* IT, SOLDIER. WITH *PETER* ON MY ARM, I FEEL LIKE A *SWEEPSTAKES WINNER*.

MMMM... IF YOU'RE ALL *THAT* GROOVY, MAYBE YOU DESERVE *MARY JANE.*

WHEN WOULD YOU *LIKE* HIM, DEAR? BEFORE OR *AFTER* I PULL YOUR *HAIR* OUT?

LOOK, GORGEOUS... IF YOU'RE IN THE MOOD TO PICK UP *STRAYS,* HOW ABOUT *ME?*

WE CAN *STILL* KEEP PUNY PARKER AROUND FOR *LAUGHS!*

THAT *DOES* IT, WISE GUY. IF YOU THINK YOUR *UNIFORM* GIVES YOU THE RIGHT TO...

CLAM UP, CHOWDER-HEAD, BEFORE I GIVE YOU A *KNUCKLE SANDWICH* TO CHEW ON.

PETE... FLASH... *STOP* IT.

I'VE GOTTA TAKE *OFF.* I'M SO *UPTIGHT,* THAT THE SLIGHTEST *REMARK* COULD MAKE ME BLOW MY STACK.

HEY, PETE...C'MON *BACK,* BOY. FLASH WAS ONLY CLOWNIN' AROUND!

YEAH... I *NOTICED* THE IMPROVEMENT.

THERE'S SOMETHING *WORRYING* HIM. HE HASN'T BEEN HIMSELF ALL NIGHT.

FACE IT, GWEN. YOU'RE JUST HARD TO *TAKE.*

WHILE, DIRECTLY ACROSS TOWN...

YOU *HEARD* ME, ROBBIE! I WANT A FRONT PAGE *EDITORIAL* IN EVERY ISSUE...BLASTING *SPIDER-MAN.*

HE'S NOT GUESTING ON ANY TV TALK SHOW IF THE *BUGLE* CAN STOP IT.

NEVER *MIND* FREEDOM OF THE AIRWAVES. *I'M* THE BOSS HERE.

THAT'S WHY I CAME TO *SEE* YOU, JAMESON. 'CAUSE YOU'RE THE *BOSS.*

WHO IN BLUE BLAZES IS *THAT?*

NOBODY COMES INTO MY PRIVATE OFFICE UNLESS I *SAY* SO.

THEN *SAY* SO, MISTER. LET'S NOT STAND ON *CEREMONY.*

WHEN *ELECTRO* TALKS, PEOPLE *LISTEN*...AND THAT GOES FOR *YOU* TOO, JAMESON.

ELECTRO!

ELECTRO! I..I DIDN'T KNOW YOU WERE OUT OF JAIL.

STAY BACK! DON'T TOUCH ME WITH THOSE SPARKS.

RELAX, MISTER. NOBODY'S HURTIN' YOU. I JUST CAME HERE TO ASK YOU SOMETHING...

I HEARD WHAT YOU SAID ABOUT SPIDER-MAN ON TV.

WHAT WOULD IT BE WORTH TO YOU... TO HAVE HIM BEATEN AND UNMASKED ...RIGHT ON THAT SHOW?

YOU MEAN... YOU WOULD DO IT...FOR A PRICE?

YEAH. AND WITH YOUR PAPER BACKIN' ME, I'D PROBABLY GET A HERO'S MEDAL.

WHAT A STORY! WHAT A BREAK! I'LL PAY YOU A COOL THOUSAND.

MAKE IT A HOT FIVE THOUSAND.

F-FIVE THOUSAND DOLLARS?

ALL RIGHT. IT'S A DEAL. IT'LL BE WORTH IT TO ME.

AND NO TRICKS, BRILLO-HEAD.

I'LL BE BACK... FOR THE DOUGH.

IT'S TOO GOOD TO BE TRUE. I'D HAVE PAID TWENTY GRAND.

ANYTHING TO STAMP OUT THAT WALL-CRAWLING WEASEL FOREVER.

I CAN SEE THE HEADLINES NOW... "HEROIC PUBLISHER SQUASHES SPIDER-MAN!"

AND, ON THAT JOYOUS NOTE, WE TURN ONCE AGAIN TO OUR PROBLEM-RIDDEN PETER PARKER...

PETER... WAIT. WHAT IS IT? WHAT'S WRONG?

IT'S GWEN. WHAT CAN I TELL HER? HOW DO I EXPLAIN?

MAYBE... I OUGHTTA TRY TO TELL THE *TRUTH* FOR A CHANGE... AND SEE HOW IT *FEELS*.

WHAT'S *UPSETTING* YOU, PETER? *TELL* ME... IS IT... IS IT SOMETHING *I'VE* DONE?

YOU? OH *NO*, GWENDY... *NO.*

IT'S JUST THAT EVERYTHING IN MY LIFE... SEEMS TO BE GOING *WRONG*.

MY *GRADES* HAVE SLIPPED... AUNT *MAY'S* STILL WEAK...

IS THAT *ALL,* PETER?

NO... THERE'S YOU AND ME. HOW DO YOU THINK I *FEEL*... BEING TOO *BROKE* TO WINE AND DINE YOU THE WAY I *SHOULD?*

WHY SHOULD SOME-ONE LIKE YOU BE STUCK... WITH A SHNOOK LIKE *ME?*

I DON'T *CARE* HOW MUCH *MONEY* YOU HAVE. YOU'RE THE *BEST* THING THAT EVER *HAPPENED* TO ME.

DON'T *SAY* THAT!

THIS IS IT. *NOW'S* THE TIME TO FINALLY CONFESS WHAT'S *REALLY* GNAWING AT ME...

WHY CAN'T I *DO* IT? WHY CAN'T I *TELL* HER... ABOUT *SPIDER-MAN?*

OKAY, HONEY, I'LL STOP FEEL-ING *SORRY* FOR MY-SELF.

AND I'LL *HELP* YOU, MR. P.

I'D RATHER BE HERE WITH YOU... ON THIS *PARK BENCH* RIGHT NOW... THAT ANYWHERE ELSE IN THE WHOLE WIDE WORLD.

THIS IS WHY I'VE GOT TO *AMOUNT* TO SOMETHING SOME DAY.

I'VE GOT TO DO IT... FOR *GWEN*...

...FOR THE MOST *WONDERFUL* GIRL I'LL EVER KNOW.

AND, SPEAKING OF WONDERFUL PEOPLE... IT'S TIME TO VISIT *JOLLY JONAH*... JUST TWO DAYS LATER...

TELL *JOE ROBERTSON* TO COME TO MY OFFICE.

DON'T MISS OUR SPECIAL SHOW TONIGHT... GUEST-STARRING THE AMAZING *SPIDER-MAN*... IN *PERSON*.

I'VE A LITTLE *SURPRISE* FOR HIM.

AND SO, A FEW FRANTIC MINUTES LATER...

WHAT'S EVERYONE STARING AT?

YOU NEVER SAW A FELLA IN A *PAPER BAG MASK* BEFORE?

HARDWARE

LAUN

WASH and DRY

LET 'EM GAPE. THERE'S NO *LAW* AGAINST A GUY COVERING HIS *HEAD* UP.

AND THE MACHINE'S *SPINNING* TOO FAST FOR THEM TO RECOGNIZE MY *COSTUME.*

THEY'LL PROBABLY END UP FIGURING IT'S SOME NUTTY *SCHOOL INITIATION.*

FINALLY, AT THE *STUDIO* ITSELF, THE CAPACITY CROWD AWAITS SPIDEY'S APPEARANCE WITH BREATHLESS ANTICIPATION. ESPECIALLY *ONE* GRINNING GUEST...

GLAD WE GOT HERE *EARLY.* WOULDN'T WANNA MISS A *MINUTE* OF THIS.

NEVER KNEW YOU WERE SUCH A TV FAN, JAMESON.

ME? I'M A CULTURE-LOVER FROM 'WAY BACK.

AND NOW... HERE'S *MARVINNNN...*

SPIDER-MAN ISN'T *HERE* YET. WHAT DO YOU SUGGEST WE *DO?*

MAYBE WE CAN REPLACE HIM... WITH THE *BEATLES.*

OH, I SEE. *ANOTHER* INSECT'S NAME.

THAT'S RATHER *DROLL,* I SUPPOSE.

125

128

SLOWLY, INEXORABLY, THE FATEFUL SECONDS TICK BY, UNTIL....

HAVE TO GET *AWAY*... BEFORE SPIDER-MAN CAN REACH ME.

SHORT-CIRCUIT *WEAKENED* ME TOO MUCH. COULD NEVER HOPE---TO FIGHT HIM NOW.

BUT...AFTER A WHILE, I'LL *RE-CHARGE*. THEN...I'LL BIDE MY TIME...

EVERYONE'S *GONE*. THE STUDIO...IS A *SHAMBLES*.

I'VE GOT TO LEAVE, TOO. CAN'T LET ANYONE *FIND* ME...WHILE I'M THIS *WEAK*.

MY *ONE* CHANCE TO GET SOME *CASH*...AND I *BLEW* IT.

AFTER WHAT HAPPENED... I CAN *NEVER* GO BACK.

NO PRODUCER WOULD *TOUCH* ME WITH A TEN-FOOT *POLE* ANY MORE.

SO, ONCE AGAIN... SPIDER-MAN'S *HAD* IT.

EVEN MY *COSTUME* GOT SINGED... WORSE THAN EVER.

AND MY *HANDS*...ALL BRUISED AND BURNED... EVEN THROUGH MY INSULATED *GLOVES*.

IF THIS IS A *VICTORY*... I'D HATE TO BE *DEFEATED*.

...OR MAYBE I'M JUST *KIDDING* MYSELF. MAYBE I'VE *BEEN* DEFEATED.

MAYBE SPIDER-MAN'S WHOLE *CAREER* HAS JUST BEEN ONE BIG *DEFEAT*...

...AND I'VE JUST BEEN TOO *BLIND*... TO NOTICE.

WE KNOW IT'S NOT TRUE! OUR HERO IS SURE TO BE BACK BETTER THAN EVER! SO IT'S ONLY FOR THE MOMENT THAT WE SAY...

THE END

BITTEN BY A RADIOACTIVE SPIDER, STUDENT **PETER PARKER** GAINED THE PROPORTIONATE STRENGTH AND AGILITY OF AN ARACHNID! ARMED WITH HIS WONDROUS WEB-SHOOTERS, THE RELUCTANT SUPER HERO STRUGGLES WITH SINISTER SUPER-VILLAINS, MAKING ENDS MEET, AND MAINTAINING SOME SEMBLANCE OF A NORMAL LIFE!

Stan Lee PRESENTS: **THE AMAZING SPIDER-MAN**®

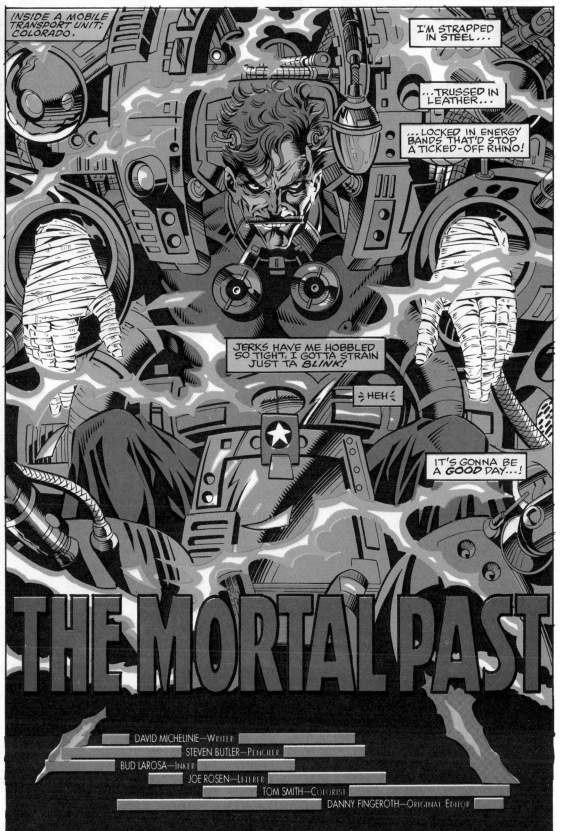

THE MORTAL PAST

DAVID MICHELINIE—Writer
STEVEN BUTLER—Penciler
BUD LAROSA—Inker
JOE ROSEN—Leterer
TOM SMITH—Colorist
DANNY FINGEROTH—Original Editor

CONRAD, PLEASE--! YOU'LL MAKE HIM ANGRY!

. . . .

AND WHEN WE REACH SEATTLE, IT SHOULD ALL BE OVER! A LAB THERE'S EXPERIMENTING WITH WAYS TO PURIFY OUTER SPACE ENVIRONMENTS--

--AND SINCE KASADY'S BLOOD WAS MUTATED BY AN ALIEN SPORE, THEY MAY BE ABLE TO CLEANSE IT--

--AND RETURN THIS LUNATIC TO WHAT, FOR HIM, PASSES AS NORMAL!

THEN YOU'LL JUST BE A SICK CREEP DOIN' ABOUT A THOUSAND YEARS OF HARD TIME!

GEE, I'M ALL TORN UP...!

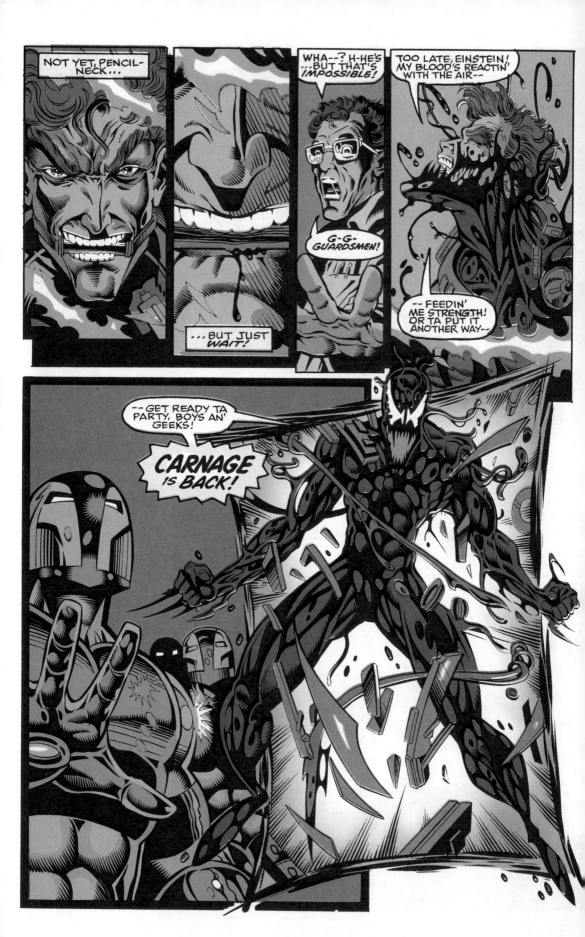

137

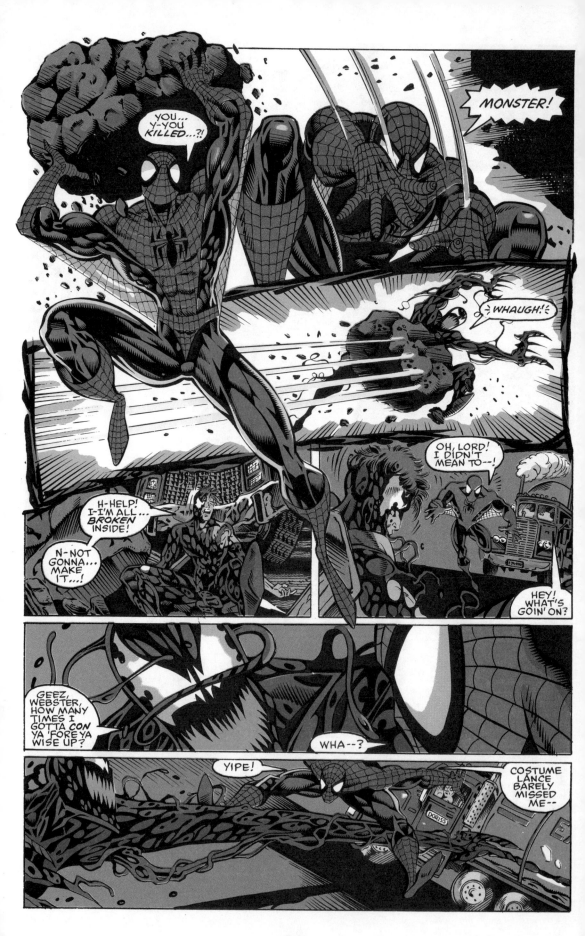

138

139

WHA--THAT *COSTUME!* I-I RECOGNIZE IT FROM THE NEWSPAPERS! IT'S YOU, ISN'T IT...*CLETE?*

BEEN KEEPIN' UP ON MY *CAREER*, BILLY?

I KNOW 'BOUT *YOU*, TOO!

THEY LET US WATCH TV EVEN IN PRISON!

YOU'RE A BIGWIG WITH THIS LUMBER COMPANY, HELPED DEVELOP SOME KINDA RADICAL *WOOD EXTENDER*--

--GOOP THAT MIXES WITH WOOD CHIPS TA MAKE BUILDIN' MATERIAL, *DOUBLIN'* THE USE O' TREES!

SUPPOSED TO BE AN ENVIRONMENTAL MILESTONE!

GOLLY, TOO BAD YA WON'T BE *ALIVE* TA SEE ALL THE GOOD IT'LL DO... AIN'T IT?

IN THE TOWN BELOW...

THERE'S THE POLICE CAR!

LARRY

AND MY *SPIDER-TRACER!* BUT--

--NO *CARNAGE!* OH, MAN...

...*WHAT NOW?*

141

144

I WASN'T GOING FOR A *WEAPON*, CLETE--

--I WAS REACHING FOR A FRESH *BOTTLE*.

EARNIN' DOUGH MUST MAKE YA THIRSTY, BILLSTER--THAT'S A LOT O' *CASH!*

GUESS LIFE'S BEEN GOOD TO YA...

...TILL *NOW!*

THAT'S ALMOST FUNNY. BUT YOU DON'T KNOW... *CAN'T* KNOW...!

SO WHY DON'T I JUST *TELL* YOU?

THINGS *WERE* GOOD: I HAD A GREAT JOB, A HAPPY MARRIAGE. THEN I WON A WEEK-END IN *VEGAS* IN AN OFFICE POOL. IT WAS SUPPOSED TO BE A FUN TRIP, A CHANGE OF PACE, AND CHANGE IT WAS--BUT NOT FOR THE *BETTER!* BECAUSE WITH THAT INNOCENT LITTLE VACATION--

THWIP

"--*TROUBLE* SWUNG INTO MY LIFE!"

146

"I GOT HOOKED ON *GAMBLING;* CARDS, DICE, IT DIDN'T MATTER. I BET ON ANYTHING-- AND USUALLY LOST!

"IT COST ME EVERYTHING: MY HOUSE, MY SAVINGS.... MY WIFE.

"I WAS IN DEBT UP TO MY EYEBALLS--

"--AND THE ONLY OUT SEEMED TO BE TO RUN AWAY, START OVER FRESH.

"WHAT'S IN THAT BRIEFCASE *WAS* IN THE COMPANY SAFE; I WAS GOING TO *MEXICO* TONIGHT."

"BUT THAT WOULD TAKE *MONEY.*

I GOTTA TELL YA, MR. BILL, I'M DISAPPOINTED. I WAS *HOPIN'* TA SHRED A RIGHTEOUS CITIZEN--

--BUT *YOU'RE* NOTHIN' BUT A WIMP, A LOSER! THIS AIN'T GONNA BE *NEARLY* AS MUCH FUN!

AW, HECK, I'LL *LIVE* WITH IT....!

≿ GASP ≾

147

THE METAL FILE CABINET IS STOPPING YOUR COSTUME DARTS, CARNAGE!

SO LET'S SEE IF IT'LL STOP *YOU* AS WELL!

KRABASH

C'MON, BILL, QUIT HOLDIN' BACK! YA GOTTA *GO*, BLAST IT! YA GOTTA--

--GO?

KNOCKED US INTA THE LUMBER MILL, WHERE THEY TURN EX-TREES INTA TWO-BY-FOURS! AN' WHERE *I'M* GONNA TURN SPIDER-MAN...

--INTA BLOODY *TOOTHPICKS!*

151

ALL RIGHT, WHAT'S ALL THE COMMO--

--TION?

GET OUT OF HERE!

SECURITY GUY'S DOIN' WHAT YA SAID, WEBS-- BUT WORRYIN' ABOUT 'IM LEFT YOU OPEN FER THIS!

GLUSH

RESH

HE'S COVERED WITH THAT RESIN GOOP! IT'S WEIGHIN' 'IM DOWN, STICKIN' 'IS ARM TO 'IS SIDE, LIKE GLUE!

HE'LL PROB'LY PULL FREE IN SECONDS!

BUT SECONDS ARE ALL I NEED...!

152

GEEZ, DID SOMEONE HIT YA WITH A *STUPID* STICK?

'COURSE CLETE'D HURT YA!

AND I DON'T NEED NOTHIN' BUT MY BARE, *HUMAN* HANDS TO BLEED *YOU!*

OKAY. DO IT...

...SPIDER-MAN!

HUH--?

SHPLOK

SAW YOU PULLIN' FREE, REMEMBERED WHAT YOU SAID ABOUT *CARNAGE* BEING TOUGH, BUT *CLETE* BEING VULNERABLE.

I TRICKED THEM.

BUT, WHY?

WHAT I SAID WAS TRUE. I'D LOST SIGHT OF WHAT REALLY MATTERS. CLETE REMINDED ME.

HE'D PROBABLY CRINGE TO HEAR IT, BUT TONIGHT...

...CLETUS KASADY WAS THE BEST *FRIEND* I'VE EVER HAD!

155

"UNMASKED by Dr. OCTOPUS!"

IN SPIDER-MAN'S LAST BATTLE AGAINST DR. OCTOPUS, THE AMAZING TEENAGER FOILED THE SUPER-VILLAIN'S PLANS, BUT HE WAS UNABLE TO PREVENT HIS ESCAPE! HENCE, THIS HEADLINE IN THE BUGLE...

DAILY BUGLE FINAL EDITION

DR. OCTOPUS ESCAPES FROM SPIDER-MAN!

PHILADELPHIA, PA. (I.P.)

ONCE AGAIN, THE MYSTERIOUS SPIDER-MAN HAS INTERFERED WITH POLICE AND ALLOWED A DANGEROUS CRIMINAL TO GET AWAY SCOT FREE!

HOW MUCH LONGER IS THIS MASKED NUISANCE TO BE PERMITTED TO MAKE A COMPLETE MOCKERY OF JUSTICE AND TO MAKE FACE A FICTION OUT OF ALL THE POLICE IN ALL IN THE ENTIRE DISTRICT OF...

SPIDER-MAN... OVERRATED CRIME-FIGHTER!

DR. OCTOPUS... STILL AT LARGE!

READING THE NEWS ITEM, WHICH WAS OBVIOUSLY WRITTEN BY ORDER OF PUBLISHER J. JONAH JAMESON WHO HATES SPIDER-MAN, THE ANGRY ADVENTURER DECIDES TO PAY JAMESON A VISIT...

IF I PUT OUT A FOREST FIRE SINGLE-HANDED, I'LL BET JONAH WOULD RAP ME FOR WASTING TOO MUCH WATER! SAY! WHAT'S GOING ON IN HIS OFFICE?

I QUIT! NOBODY COULD WORK FOR A TYRANT LIKE YOU!

THAT'S THE GAL HE HIRED TO FILL IN TILL BETTY RETURNED FROM PHILADELPHIA!

WAIT! YOU CAN'T DO THIS! I NEED A SECRETARY! COME BACK!

YOU DON'T NEED A SECRETARY-- YOU NEED A PSYCHIATRIST!

HMMPH! BLAMED EMPLOYEES! THEY EXPECT TO BE TREATED WITH KID GLOVES! JUST BECAUSE I SHOUTED AT HER...

HELLO, MR. JAMESON! I'VE RETURNED--THAT IS, IF YOU STILL WANT ME?

BETTY BRANT! IF I WANT YOU?? DON'T JUST STAND THERE, GIRL-- GET TO WORK!

NOW THAT BETTY'S BACK, I'LL CHANGE TO PETER PARKER. I CAN'T WAIT TO SEE HER-- TO TALK TO HER...

MR. JAMESON, HAS PETER PARKER BEEN IN LATELY WITH ANY PHOTOS?

NO! I HAVEN'T SEEN HIM! HE'S PROBABLY TOO LAZY TO WORK... JUST LIKE EVERYONE ELSE I GET STUCK WITH!

MINUTES LATER...

BETTY! GOSH, I'M GLAD TO SEE YOU! I'VE BEEN WAITING TO HEAR FROM YOU...

OUT, PARKER! THIS IS AN OFFICE, NOT A SOCIAL CLUB! YOU CAN COME IN HERE WHENEVER YOU HAVE A SET OF EXCLUSIVE NEWS PHOTOS FOR ME, AND NOT BEFORE! NOW GET!

I'LL SEE YOU LATER, PETER! CALL ME AT HOME!

STAN LEE—Writer
STEVE DITKO—Penciler
ART SIMEK—Letterer

MEANWHILE, AT DIFFERENT PLACES THRUOUT THE NATION, MOVING FROM CITY TO CITY LIKE THE ELUSIVE MARAUDER HE IS, THE AWESOME *DR. OCTOPUS* ATTEMPTS SOME OF THE MOST COLORFUL CRIMES EVER PERPETRATED!

EVEN AN ARMORED CAR IS NO MATCH FOR MY POWER!

EACH ESCAPE IS NARROWER THAN THE LAST, BUT I CAN'T STOP NOW!

THE POLICE HAVE BEEN ALERTED TO ME! I DARE NOT USE THE SAME TRICKS TWICE!

I'VE GOT TO CONTINUE MY SPECTACULAR CAREER, SO THAT *SPIDER-MAN* WILL READ ABOUT MY EXPLOITS AND TRY TO ATTACK ME AGAIN!

I *KNOW* I'M STRONGER THAN HE IS! I KNOW THAT I'LL DESTROY HIM WHEN NEXT WE MEET! BUT, SO LONG AS HE LIVES, I'LL NEVER BE TRULY SAFE! I'VE *GOT* TO FORCE HIM TO FIGHT ME AGAIN!

BUT WHY HASN'T HE FOLLOWED ME? I'VE GIVEN HIM EVERY CHANCE -- ALL THE BAIT HE NEEDS! PERHAPS I'LL HAVE TO RETURN TO NEW YORK AND FIND *HIM!*

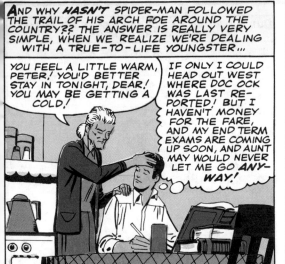

AND WHY *HASN'T* SPIDER-MAN FOLLOWED THE TRAIL OF HIS ARCH FOE AROUND THE COUNTRY?? THE ANSWER IS REALLY VERY SIMPLE, WHEN WE REALIZE WE'RE DEALING WITH A TRUE-TO-LIFE YOUNGSTER...

YOU FEEL A LITTLE WARM, PETER! YOU'D BETTER STAY IN TONIGHT, DEAR! YOU MAY BE GETTING A COLD!

IF ONLY I COULD HEAD OUT WEST WHERE DOC OCK WAS LAST RE-PORTED! BUT I HAVEN'T MONEY FOR THE FARE, AND MY END TERM EXAMS ARE COMING UP SOON, AND AUNT MAY WOULD NEVER LET ME GO ANY-WAY!

THE NEXT DAY...

OH WELL, MAYBE OCTOPUS WILL RETURN TO NEW YORK SOMEDAY, AND THEN -- SAY! I WONDER WHAT THE KIDS ARE READING ABOUT?

HOW DO YOU LIKE *THIS?* THE DAILY BUGLE IS *STILL* WRIT-ING EDITORIALS CALLING SPIDER-MAN A FAKE AND A COWARD!

THAT'S EASY FOR JAMESON TO SAY! I'D LIKE TO SEE *HIM* TACKLE DR. OCTOPUS!

I WONDER IF WE'LL EVER FIND OUT WHO SPIDER-MAN REALLY *IS?*

LOOK, THE BUGLE EVEN HAS A PICTURE OF A SPIDER, TRYING TO SHOW HOW DANGEROUS THEY ARE, AND CLAIMING THAT *SPIDER-MAN* MUST BE DANGEROUS, TOO!

HERE COMES BOOK-WORM PARKER! LET'S SEE WHAT *HE* KNOWS ABOUT SPIDERS!

I'VE GOT TO BE CAREFUL NOT TO SAY ANYTHING THAT'LL MAKE THEM SUSPECT MY REAL IDENTITY!

I *HATE* SPIDERS! THEY'RE SUCH UGLY, ICKY-LOOKING THINGS! I'D RATHER NOT EVEN *TALK* ABOUT THEM!

KNOW WHAT I LIKE ABOUT YOU, PARKER? YOU'RE SUCH A RUGGED, FEAR-LESS HE-MAN!

C'MON, GANG! THERE'S THE BELL FOR CLASS!

SOMEONE TAKE PARKER'S ARM! HE MAY STEP ON AN ANTHILL AND FAINT DEAD AWAY!

GO AHEAD, *LAUGH*, YOU BIRD-BRAINED CLOWN! SOMEDAY EVERYONE WILL REALIZE THAT IT'S ONLY THE PEOPLE WHO ARE INFERIOR *THEM-SELVES* THAT KEEP PICKING ON OTHERS!

HOW *ABOUT* THAT? I'M BEGINNIN' TO SOUND LIKE A TEEN-AGE BILLY GRAHAM!

NOT LONG AFTERWARDS, BETTY BRANT RECEIVES A MYSTERIOUS PHONE CALL...

YES, THIS IS SHE! HELLO? WHO'S THERE?

HELLO? WHY DON'T YOU ANSWER--??

AND, AT THE OTHER END OF THE WIRE...

GOOD! NOW THAT I KNOW SHE IS BACK WORKING FOR THE DAILY BUGLE, I'LL BE ABLE TO USE *HER* AS BAIT TO CATCH SPIDER-MAN! HE RISKED HIS LIFE TO HELP HER ONCE BEFORE... SO WHY NOT AGAIN?✱

HE HUNG UP! IT SOUNDED LIKE-- OH NO! THAT'S IMPOSSIBLE! IT *CAN'T* BE!

GET TO *WORK*, MISS BRANT! I DON'T PAY YOU TO DAY-DREAM!

THEN, TOWARDS THE END OF THE DAY...

YOU AGAIN?? I THOUGHT I TOLD YOU TO STAY OUT UNLESS YOU HAD SOME NEWS PHOTOS FOR ME!

SORRY, MR. JAMESON! I JUST CAME BY TO CALL FOR BETTY!

BE WITH YOU IN A MINUTE, PETER... SOON AS I FINISH THIS LETTER!

BUT SUDDENLY, A MOCKING, MENACING FORM APPEARS AT THE WINDOW...

I WOULDN'T HOLD MY BREATH WAITING IF I WERE YOU, SONNY! I'VE GOT *OTHER* PLANS FOR HER!

DOCTOR OCTOPUS! HERE IN NEW YORK!!

THEN-- IT *WAS* YOUR VOICE ON THE PHONE BEFORE!!

4

AND THEN, AS A SPECIAL, EXTRA EDITION OF THE BUGLE HITS THE NEWSSTANDS...

GET DOWN TO CONEY ISLAND, PARKER! WAIT FOR SPIDER-MAN TO SHOW UP! BRING PLENTY OF FILM! IF YOU BOTCH THIS ASSIGNMENT, I'LL HAVE YOUR HIDE!

DON'T WORRY-- NOTHING COULD KEEP ME AWAY!

STRANGE-- I FEEL KIND OF WOOSY-- MY HEAD IS WARM-- MAYBE I AM GETTING ILL, AS AUNT MAY SAID!

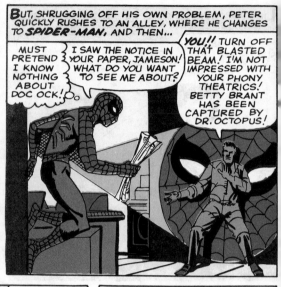

BUT, SHRUGGING OFF HIS OWN PROBLEM, PETER QUICKLY RUSHES TO AN ALLEY, WHERE HE CHANGES TO SPIDER-MAN, AND THEN...

MUST PRETEND I KNOW NOTHING ABOUT DOC OCK!

I SAW THE NOTICE IN YOUR PAPER, JAMESON! WHAT DO YOU WANT TO SEE ME ABOUT?

YOU!! TURN OFF THAT BLASTED BEAM! I'M NOT IMPRESSED WITH YOUR PHONY THEATRICS! BETTY BRANT HAS BEEN CAPTURED BY DR. OCTOPUS!

THEN, AFTER JAMESON HAS EXPLAINED...

NOW FOR CONEY ISLAND! HEY-- I MUST BE SICK! I-I'M NOT CLINGING TO THE WALL AS WELL AS USUAL!

MEANWHILE... EVEN THOUGH PARKER IS MY BEST FREE-LANCE PHOTOGRAPHER, I CAN'T TAKE ANY CHANCE OF HIM MUFFING THIS JOB! MAYBE I'D BETTER GET TO CONEY ISLAND MYSELF!

IT'S MID-WINTER, SO THE AMUSEMENTS WILL ALL BE SHUT DOWN FOR THE SEASON! I'LL MAKE SURE THAT DR. OCTOPUS DOESN'T SEE ME, BUT I'LL HAVE A CHANCE TO OBSERVE WHATEVER HAPPENS, FIRST HAND!

AND, ATOP THE HIGHEST ROLLER COASTER AT THE AMUSEMENT PARK...

SPIDER-MAN SHOULD HAVE SEEN THE PAPER BY NOW! THAT MEANS HE'LL BE ARRIVING AT ANY MOMENT-- FOR HIS FINAL BATTLE!

B-BUT WHAT IF HE DOESN'T SHOW UP?

THAT WILL BE TOO BAD, MY DEAR! FOR YOU! AND NOW, I'LL LOWER YOU TO THE GROUND, SO THE PHOTOGRAPHER CAN EASILY GET GOOD PICTURES OF MY VICTORY OVER THAT MASKED FOOL! THOSE PICTURES, FOR THE WORLD TO SEE, WILL BE SPIDER-MAN'S GREATEST HUMILIATION!

6

THE PHOTOGRAPHER ISN'T HERE YET! HE'D BETTER SHOW UP, OR HE'LL LIVE TO REGRET IT!

PERHAPS IF I KEEP PRYING AT THE KNOT WITH MY LONG FINGERNAILS, I CAN FREE MYSELF WHILE DR. OCTOPUS ISN'T LOOKING!

AND, ENTERING THE PARK AT THAT MOMENT...

CAN HARDLY STAND--MY FEET FEEL LIKE RUBBER! OF ALL THE TIMES FOR ME TO GET A VIRUS ATTACK...

BUT I CAN'T LET IT STOP ME! I'VE GOT TO SAVE BETTY--GOT TO FIND DR. OCTOPUS...

IF ONLY I DIDN'T FEEL SO WEAK! IF I COULD JUST LIE DOWN FOR--

WAIT! THERE HE IS! I'VE GOT TO GO THRU WITH IT NOW!

I DID IT! I'M FREE! NOW IF I CAN JUST REACH THE STREET IN TIME....!

SO! YOU THINK YOU CAN ESCAPE ME, DO YOU! THIS TIME I SHALL NOT BE SO FORGIVING!

HE'S REACHING FOR BETTY! IT'S NOW OR NEVER!

HOLD IT, OCTOPUS! I'M THE ONE YOU WANT-- AND NOW I'VE GOT YOU!

TOO WEAK FOR A LONG BATTLE! I'VE GOT TO KNOCK HIM OUT WITH THE FIRST PUNCH! IT'S MY ONLY CHANCE!

OH--NO! I TRIED MY BEST, BUT MY SPIDER STRENGTH IS GONE! IT WAS JUST A WEAK, MEANINGLESS PUNCH --HE HARDLY FELT IT!

WHAT SORT OF STUNT IS THIS, SPIDER-MAN? I KNOW YOU CAN HIT HARDER THAN THAT! IF THIS IS SOME SORT OF TRICK, IT'LL DO YOU NO GOOD--YOU WON'T BE GIVEN A SECOND CHANCE!

7

BAH!! TAKE YOUR PUNY HERO! HE'S OF NO INTEREST TO ME! IT'S THE REAL SPIDER-MAN I'M AFTER!!

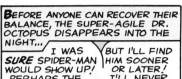

BEFORE ANYONE CAN RECOVER THEIR BALANCE, THE SUPER-AGILE DR. OCTOPUS DISAPPEARS INTO THE NIGHT...

I WAS SURE SPIDER-MAN WOULD SHOW UP! PERHAPS THE POLICE SCARED HIM OFF!

BUT I'LL FIND HIM SOONER OR LATER! I'LL NEVER REST TILL I'VE SMASHED HIM!

JAMESON, NEXT TIME YOU WITHHOLD INFORMATION FROM US, IT'LL GO HARD WITH YOU! IF YOU HAD TOLD US ABOUT THIS, WE WOULD HAVE SET A TRAP FOR OCTOPUS AND CAUGHT HIM BY NOW!

BUT YOU THOUGHT MORE OF AN EXCLUSIVE STORY THAN ANYTHING ELSE!

OH, PETER-- PETER! YOU DEAR, FOOLISH, WONDERFUL BOY!! WHY DID YOU DO IT?? IF ANYTHING HAD HAPPENED TO YOU--!!

I BETTER NOT YELL AT PARKER NOW, IN FRONT OF THE POLICE! THEY'RE ANGRY ENOUGH AT ME NOW! THIS SURE WAS ONE BIG FLOP!!

HE'LL BE ALRIGHT, MISS! WE'LL SEE THAT HE GETS HOME SAFELY! HE'S A PRETTY BRAVE KID, IMPERSON-ATING SPIDER-MAN AND TACKLING DR. OCTOPUS LIKE THAT!

HOURS LATER, AT HOME...

POOR BOY! A NICE POLICEMAN BROUGHT HIM HOME! HE SAID HE HAD FAINTED IN THE STREET! I KNEW HE WAS COM-ING DOWN WITH SOMETHING!

NOTHING TO WORRY ABOUT, MRS. PARKER! IT'S JUST THE TWENTY-FOUR HOUR VIRUS! IT MAKES ONE WEAK AS A KITTEN FOR A DAY, BUT THEN IT PASSES! HE'LL BE FINE IN THE MORNING!

AS PETER SLEEPS, HIS REST IS BROKEN BY A TROUBLED DREAM...

WHAT ARE YOU? SOME KINDA NUT OR SOMETHING?? YOU SHOULD HAVE YOUR HEAD EXAMINED FOR APPEARING AS SPIDER-MAN WHEN YOU WERE SO WEAK! YOU KNOW THAT VIRUSES ARE THE ONE THING EVEN YOUR SPIDER STRENGTH CAN'T RESIST!

BUT-- I WAS SO WORRIED-- ABOUT BETTY-- SO WORRIED--

THEN, COMES THE NEXT MORNING -- MORE THAN TWENTY-FOUR HOURS AFTER THE VIRUS HAS STRUCK...

WHOOPEE! I FEEL LIKE A ZILLION BUCKS AGAIN!

I'VE GOT THE OL' SPIDER STRENGTH BACK! THE OL' ZINGAROOO!

9

UH OH!! MY *SPIDER-MAN* OUTFIT!! THE POLICE MUST HAVE SENT IT TO AUNT MAY! SHE MUST HAVE *SEEN* IT! I'LL HAVE TO MOVE FAST!

PETER! DID I HEAR YOU MOVING AROUND UP THERE?? I'M COMING UP! I WANT TO *SPEAK* TO YOU!

I RECEIVED A STRANGE COSTUME FROM THE POLICE THIS MORNING-- AND I HEARD WHAT *REALLY* HAPPENED TO YOU LAST NIGHT! HOW COULD YOU *POSSIBLY* TAKE SUCH A CHANCE, IMPERSONATING THAT *DREADFUL* SPIDER-MAN!!

LOOK, AUNT MAY, I'M SORRY! I'LL NEVER DO IT AGAIN! HERE, I'M GONNA TAKE THAT SILLY COSTUME OUT AND *BURN* IT!

HOPE SHE DOESN'T SUSPECT I'VE STUFFED THIS BUNDLE WITH *RAGS!* I'M *WEARING* MY COSTUME UNDER MY SUIT!

LATER, AT SCHOOL...

HEY, LOOK! HERE COMES THE BIG "HERO"!! FEARLESS PARKER, IN THE FLESH!!

I *KNEW* IT! FLASH'LL NEVER LET ME LIVE IT DOWN!

PETER, WE ALL HEARD ABOUT LAST NIGHT!! WHY DID YOU EVER TRY TO IMPERSONATE *SPIDER-MAN??*

IF YOU DON'T MIND, LIZ-- I'D RATHER NOT TALK ABOUT IT!

BUT I THINK IT WAS THE MOST *WONDERFUL* THING I'VE EVER HEARD OF!

AW, QUIT *KIDDIN'*, LIZ! EVERYONE *KNOWS* PARKER NEVER EXPECTED TO REALLY BUMP INTO OCTOPUS! HE WAS JUST TRYIN' TO SHOW OFF-- FOR KICKS!

LET ME TELL *YOU* SOMETHING, FLASH THOMPSON! AS FAR AS *I'M* CONCERNED, PETER PARKER PROVED HE HAS ENOUGH COURAGE TO MATCH HIS *BRAINS!* AND AS FOR *YOU*, MY DEAR *EX-BOY* FRIEND, YOU'VE GOT *NEITHER!!*

HOLY SMOKE! WHAT CHANGED LIZ ALLEN?? SHE NEVER EVEN KNEW I WAS *ALIVE!!*

GOSH, LIZ!! WHAT'RE YOU MAD AT *ME* FOR??

*M*EANWHILE, AN ANGRY *DR. OCTOPUS* RIPS THE NEWSPAPERS TO SHREDS IN A FIT OF SAVAGE FURY...

THEY'RE MAKING A LAUGHING STOCK OF ME!! SAYING THAT I WAS FOOLED BY A *TEEN-AGER!*

WELL, THEY'LL ALL BE LAUGHING OUT OF THE OTHER SIDES OF THEIR MOUTHS BEFORE *I'M* THRU WITH THEM!

10

SPIDER-MAN WILL BE ABLE TO HIDE FROM ME NO LONGER! I'LL *MAKE* HIM COME TO ME -- IF IT'S THE LAST THING I *DO!*

I'M THRU WITH HIDING OUT!! I FEAR *NOBODY!* I'M THE MOST POWERFUL ONE IN THE CITY!

I'LL LEAVE MY BASEMENT HIDEOUT AND MAKE SURE THAT NEW YORK NEVER FORGETS THIS DAY -- NEVER FORGETS THE POWER OF *DR. OCTOPUS!!*

NO PARK-ING

LATER, AT THE OUTSKIRTS OF THE ZOO...

RUN!! THE WILD BEASTS ARE LOOSE!!! *DR. OCTOPUS* SET THEM ALL FREE!!

HELP!! SOMEBODY *HELP!!*

WITHIN SECONDS, THE POLICE ARE ON THE SCENE, WORKING VALIANTLY TO TRAP THE RAMPAGING BEASTS BEFORE ANYONE CAN BE INJURED!!

CAREFUL, JOE! THIS BABY'S A *KILLER!!*

WE CAN'T *AFFORD* TO BE CAREFUL, BILL! TOO MANY LIVES MAY BE AT STAKE!!

MEANWHILE, A SHORT DISTANCE AWAY...

THIS IS *NUTS!* LIZ WOULDN'T GIVE ME A TUMBLE BEFORE --BUT NOW SHE'S FOLLOWIN' ME AROUND LIKE A LOVESICK CALF!

PETER, WAIT FOR ME! I'LL WALK HOME WITH YOU! I WANT TO ASK YOU SOMETHING...

LIZ -- WAIT! I THOUGHT WE WERE GOIN' *BOWLING* THIS AFTERNOON! LIZ --!!

11

THEN, QUICKLY ROUNDING A CORNER, THE AMAZING TEEN-AGER MOVES LIKE A STREAK...

NO ONE'S LOOKING! NOW'S MY CHANCE!

PETE'S GONE! I LOST HIM! FLASH THOMPSON! I'LL THANK YOU TO STOP FOLLOWING ME!

BUT, LIZ, YOU CAN'T BE SERIOUS ABOUT PUNY PARKER!! HE'S NOT YOUR TYPE! YOU USED TO SAY SO YOURSELF!

WELL, PERHAPS I'VE GROWN MATURE ENOUGH TO REALIZE A BOY NEEDS MORE THAN A FOOTBALL LETTER TO REALLY BE A MAN!

SAY-- WHAT'S ALL THAT SHOUTING UP AHEAD! I'D BETTER HAVE A LOOK!

WOW! THAT LION MUST HAVE ESCAPED FROM THE ZOO! IT'S ABOUT TO ATTACK THAT CROWD OF PEOPLE!!

A LION!! HELP!

RUN! HE'S GOING TO LEAP AT US!!

I'VE NEVER FOUGHT ANYTHING LIKE THIS BEFORE-- BUT THERE'S ALWAYS A FIRST TIME!!

HERE COME THE POLICE-- WITH A NET!

HE'S ALL YOURS, FELLAS!

QUICK! GET THE NET AROUND HIM!!

MUCH OBLIGED, SPIDER-MAN! WE'VE HAD OUR HANDS FULL WITH THESE ESCAPED BEASTS!

ESCAPED BEASTS?? THAT MEANS THERE'S MORE!! UH-OH!! HERE'S ANOTHER ONE NOW!

12

167

WELL, WELL!! SO SPIDER-MAN FINALLY CAME OUT OF HIDING AT LAST!! UNLESS IT'S THAT IDIOTIC PETER PARKER AGAIN,!!

DON'T *SAY* THAT, MR. JAMESON! IT *MUSTN'T* BE PETER -- IT JUST *MUSTN'T*!!

BUT JAMESON AND BETTY BRANT ARE *BOTH* RIGHT! IT *IS* THE REAL SPIDER-MAN... AND IT'S *ALSO* PETER PARKER -- ALTHOUGH *THIS* TIME NOBODY SUSPECTS THE TRUTH!!

ALL RIGHT, OCTOPUS!! YOU'VE BEEN *ASKING* FOR ANOTHER TANGLE WITH ME -- AND NOW YOU'RE GONNA *GET* IT!

SPIDER-MAN!! AT LAST!!

THIS TIME, YOU WEB-SHOOTING FREAK, I'LL SHOW YOU NO MERCY!!

WHAT DO YOU MEAN *THIS* TIME?? A FLORENCE NIGHTINGALE YOU'VE *NEVER* BEEN!

AND, A FEW STORIES BELOW --

BLAST HIM! THAT'S THE *REAL* SPIDER-MAN, ALL RIGHT!! PARKER WOULD NEVER HAVE HAD THE *NERVE* TO SOAK ME THAT WAY!

OHH, MISTER JAMESON!! DR. OCTOPUS IS SO MUCH BIGGER -- SO MUCH *MORE* VICIOUS! WHAT CHANCE WILL SPIDER-MAN HAVE??

AND SPIDER-MAN *TOO* ASKS HIMSELF THAT QUESTION...

THOSE BLAMED *ARMS* OF HIS MAKE HIM STRONGER THAN I! HOW AM I GONNA FIGURE OUT A WAY TO DEFEAT HIM ONCE AND FOR ALL??

WELL, *ONE* THING'S FOR SURE -- I'D BETTER COME UP WITH AN *ANSWER* PRETTY DARN FAST!

I'VE *GOT* YOU NOW! YOU'VE NO PLACE TO RUN!!

15

172

MY ONLY CHANCE IS TO USE MY WEB! I'LL MAKE A FIRE SHIELD OUT OF--OH *NO!!* I'M OUT OF FLUID,!!!

I'VE GOT SPARE CARTRIDGES IN MY BELT--IF ONLY I CAN *USE* THEM IN TIME,!!

THE FLAME'S GETTING CLOSER--HAVE TO MOVE FASTER--GOOD THING I'VE PRACTICED THIS SO OFTEN--COULD DO IT IN MY SLEEP,!!

THERE!! IT'S ALL LOADED!! NOW TO PRESS THE RELEASE BUTTON, AND KEEP MY FINGERS CROSSED!!!

HERE GOES!!

USING HIS AMAZING SPIDER-WEB LIKE A VIRTUOSO, PLAYING OUT JUST THE RIGHT AMOUNT OF FLUID AT JUST THE RIGHT SPLIT-SECOND, SPIDER-MAN MANAGES TO CREATE A FLAME-PROOF UMBRELLA FOR HIS HEAD, PLUS SOME SECTIONS OF WEBBING TO USE AS STEPPING STONES FOR HIS RACING FEET!!

IT'S WORKING! NOW, IF I CAN JUST REACH THE WINDOW--!!

MADE IT!! I'LL CLING TO THE WALL OF THIS BUILDING NEXT DOOR AND SWING TO SAFETY FROM HERE!

21

THERE ARE THE FIRE ENGINES BELOW!! WONDER IF THEY CAN GET TO DOC OCK IN TIME???

REACHING THE STREET, SPIDER-MAN DUCKS INTO A NEARBY DOORWAY, EMERGING SECONDS LATER AS OUR TEEN-AGE FRIEND, PETER PARKER!

LOOK! IT'S PETER! I'VE BEEN LOOKING FOR YOU!! YOU MISSED ALL THE EXCITEMENT!

GET LOST, PARKER! DOC. OCTOPUS IS STILL AT LARGE! YOU MIGHT SEE HIM AND FAINT DEAD AWAY FROM FRIGHT!

WHY DON'T YOU SLITHER BACK TO THE ROCK YOU CRAWLED OUT FROM UNDER, FLASH!

HEY! THERE'S DOCTOR OCTOPUS!! HE LOOKS HALF DEAD!

HE'S ALL YOURS, PAL! WE DON'T WANT HIM!

WELL, WE DO! WE'VE BEEN ITCHIN' TO GET OUR HANDS ON THIS CHARACTER!

ALL RIGHT, MISTER, KEEP MOVING! WE'VE GOT A NICE COZY CELL FOR YOU TO RECUPERATE IN!

SPIDER-MAN DIDN'T BEAT ME! IT WAS THE FIRE! IF NOT FOR THE FIRE, EVERYTHING WOULD HAVE BEEN DIFFERENT!!

SURE, SURE! EVERY TIME YOU'VE MET SPIDER-MAN, HE'S STOPPED YOU COLD! BUT NEXT TIME'LL BE DIFFERENT-- WE KNOW!!

NOW THEN, PETER, WHAT I WANTED TO ASK YOU WAS-- I'M HAVING A PARTY TONIGHT, AND...

SORRY, LIZ! NO CAN DO! I'VE GOT A DATE WITH A CERTAIN LITTLE BRUNETTE TONIGHT, EVEN THOUGH SHE MAY NOT KNOW IT YET!

I'M SURE FLASH WILL BE HAPPY TO GO INSTEAD OF ME! ALTHOUGH I KNOW HOW BORING IT MUST BE TO HAVE TO USE ALL THOSE ONE-SYLLABLE WORDS WHEN YOU TALK TO HIM! ANYWAY, YOU DESERVE EACH OTHER!

WHY, THAT CRUMMY--!!

DON'T SAY IT, FLASH! WE RATED THAT, AFTER THE WAY WE'VE ALWAYS TREATED PETER!

AND, LATER THAT NIGHT...

LUCKILY, I HAD THE AUTOMATIC SHUTTER OF MY CAMERA WORKING DURING MY FIGHT WITH DOC OCK, SO OL' TIGHTWAD JAMESON PAID ME A BUNDLE FOR THE PIX! YES SIREE, THINGS ARE SURE LOOKING UP FOR MY FAVORITE COUPLE OF GUYS--NAMELY ME!

FOOLED YOU, EH? SEE, WE DON'T ALWAYS HAVE UNHAPPY ENDINGS! LIKE ANYONE ELSE, OUR WEB-SPINNIN' HERO HAS HIS UPS AND DOWNS! AND THOUGH THINGS MAY BE ROSY, NOTHING STAYS THE SAME FOR VERY LONG! BUT, FOR NOW, IT'S DEFINITELY...

THE END